G000300789

THE CAR BUILDER'S HANDBOOK

Kit Car
ELECTRICS

First published 1997
Second edition published March 1999
Copyright Blueprint Books Ltd

ISBN 1 899814 20 5

Published by
Blueprint Books Ltd., 1 Howard Road, Reigate, Surrey RH2 7JE
Tel: 01737 225565   Fax: 01737 240185

Computer Graphics and repro by Brooklands Publishing Ltd, Dormansland
Editing and page design by Ian Stent
Printed by Grapevine Print & Marketing Ltd.

Other books of interest to the kit car enthusiast include:

CLASSIC KIT CARS - A comprehensive buyer's guide to every kit car produced between 1953 and 1985. A simply amazing reference book for the kit car devotee. Over 450 photographs. UK price: £18.00 inc p&p. (£23.00 for hardback limited edition signed by the author).

THREE-WHEELERS - Here's a complete history of trikes, from 1885 right up to the current day. With over 160 pages and 300 photographs it is surely the most comprehensive look at the barmy world of three-wheelers. An absolute must. UK price: £18.00 inc p&p.

COBRA REPLICAS - Part of the *Kit Car Collection* series, here's a book devoted to the current crop of fake snakes. Road tests of each manufacturer's car tell you just what it is like to pilot these thunderous machines. 120 pages, 100s of pictures, many in colour. UK price: £11.95 inc p&p.

THE WHICH KIT? GUIDE - This annually updated publication is a great introduction to the kit car industry. All the major manufacturers are listed, along with details of the donor cars required, kit contents, budget on-the-road costs and current addresses and brochure prices etc. UK Price: £6.95 inc p&p.

THE WHICH KIT? GUIDE TO KIT CAR BUILDING - Dealing with everything from initial factory visits and choosing your kit right through to final registration once the car is complete, you won't find a more comprehensive and informative book on the art of building kit cars. UK price: £18.50 inc p&p.

Any of these books can be ordered by credit card from mail order specialists, Bluestream Books. For further information or a full listing of other car books available, contact:
Bluestream Books, 1 Howard Road, Reigate, Surrey RH2 7JE
Tel: 01737 222030   Fax: 01737 240185

CONTENTS

Introduction

INSTALLING THE ELECTRICS ON A KIT CAR IS OFTEN regarded with apprehension, sometimes even approaching dread, by many home car builders. They'll happily tackle an engine or suspension rebuild, and coping with tricky problems on the body is child's play. But confront them with a bunch of multi-coloured spaghetti under the dash and down comes the heavy weight on the shoulders together with a little nagging voice in the subconscious that keeps saying "I hope you've connected the right wire to that terminal because, let's face it, you don't really know what you're doing, do you?"

If this sounds only too familiar, take heart. After you've read this book the weight will lift and the little nagging voice will be silent. Read the next sentence carefully and learn it by heart. *Car electrics aren't complicated.* Complex, maybe (certainly more complex than they were years ago because of all the electrical extras that we now regard as essential) but not complicated.

Just in case you're not sure about the difference between those two words, I'll quote from my dictionary. Complex: made up of various interconnected parts. Complicated: made up of intricate parts that are difficult to understand or analyse. Car electrics are certainly interconnected but, provided you understand a simple circuit of battery, feed,

Below: This simple little Sylva Striker is a typical kit you might decide to design your own wiring loom for. Alternatively, you could buy a purpose designed loom or modify your donor car's wiring harness.

When you're using a modern engine like this Cosworth turbo, your kit car's wiring will become considerably more complex. You must also be very careful to get the engine's dedicated wiring harness as it is often impossible to make these up from scratch.

switch, component and return, they aren't difficult to understand or to analyse. If you can wire up a push-bike dynamo, you can wire up a car.

Many car builders will either use a new wiring loom supplied by the kit maker, or modify the loom from the donor car, but even then you have to know how to read a wiring diagram. At first glance these look terribly complicated but, once again, they aren't, they're just complex, and seem even more complex because they use diagrammatic forms such as positive and negative rails with the position of the components in the diagram bearing no relation to the position they're in on the car. This book will show you how to interpret them and how to sort out the various circuits in a complex diagram so that the complexity drops away and they become a collection of simple circuits. It will even show you, if you fancy it, how to design and construct your own wiring diagram from scratch.

Wiring, however, is only one part of dealing with electrics on a car build. Apart from the chassis and body, building a kit car involves putting together a lot of secondhand components from a donor car, and this includes all the electrical components. Standard production cars have plenty of problems with electrical components, and the

Above: The most concentrated area of wiring in most cars centres around the dashboard. Having lots of gauges and switches will inevitably mean more wiring. Be methodical.

A mid-engined kit such as this Stratos replica will introduce further complexities to a wiring harness. None of the problems is insurmountable, you'll just have to be a little more careful.

chances are that your donor car will have had, and may even still have, its fair share. You could, of course, shell out lots of dosh and buy all new or rebuilt electrical components with a reasonable expectation of having no further problems other than a rapidly diminishing bank balance. Fine if you can afford it, but most of us can't, which is why we buy a donor car. In this book, I'll cover not just the wiring up of the components, I'll show you how to strip and overhaul them with the accent always on saving money.

Don't be put off by the storeman in a main dealer telling you that various components aren't repairable. What he means is that the parts to repair them aren't listed on his microfiche because, with garage labour at £20 an hour plus, the cost of repair would be higher than the cost of a new part. When you don't count your time, the cost to put a non-working electrical component back into working order can often be negligible. In may cases all that's needed is a strip and clean. This book will show you how to go about it.

So welcome to the world of wiring looms, relays, switches and motors. Push your apprehensions aside and tackle the subject with enthusiasm. It's a fascinating and logical world. And, once you're at home in it, you'll have

Above: This beautiful Royale Sabre is almost completely based around the Ford Granada/Scorpio range and retains the donor's wiring loom. You'll still be making a few modifications for the period dash instruments. This book will tell you how.

the satisfaction of knowing that if, in the future, something goes wrong, you won't have to call in a very expensive auto electrician to sort it out for you.

Chapter 1

ESSENTIAL BASICS

Some of this chapter is basics, but don't skip it - it's essential stuff.

THE ELECTRICAL SYSTEM IS PROBABLY THE ONE WHICH causes the biggest headache among kit car builders. It's often a mystery, a bit of a black art. The trouble is that, unlike something like a fuel system where you can see whether or not fuel is coming out the end of a pipe, you can't see electricity, or at least not in the same way. You can't hold up a wire and see any electricity flowing out and falling on to the floor. Though I can't see electric current or voltage, a meter can and I'll have something to say about choosing a meter in a moment. However, you won't get very far using a meter unless you understand a little about what happens in a circuit, so I want to have a few words about the basics first. I promise not to get too technical. I'll keep technicalities to a minimum and practicalities to a maximum.

Once you understand the basic principles, and they aren't hard to grasp, all the mystery disappears. My aim in this book is to show you how, in a simple and logical way, you can tackle anything on a kit car's electrics from putting in the loom to trouble shooting why a lamp doesn't light,

check and repair your main electrical components and even plan a system and wire it from scratch with confidence.

The whole key to understanding electrics is to keep in mind the difference between voltage and current, and understand the requirements of a simple circuit. I'm going to stress this, even at the risk of over-simplifying things. I'll probably make theoretical electricians throw up their hands in horror, but my aim to make it easier for you to understand a circuit and finish up with a system that works, and troubleshoot if it goes wrong.

Think of electricity as going round in a circle - that, after all, is why it's called a circuit. Electricity will flow through conductors and won't flow through non-conductors, which is simple enough. I've also got things called resistances, or resistors as electricians like to call them nowadays, which resist the flow of electricity but still let some through. These can be regarded as being in between perfect conductors and perfect non-conductors.

Having said that, there isn't such a thing as a perfect conductor. Even a length of copper wire has a certain

All circuits come in one of these two basic forms. At the top, the feed-component-switch-earth circuit is usually used for things like courtesy lights and horn pushes. Remember that the terminals at the component are live even when the switch is off. The lower feed-switch-component-earth circuit is the usual one for lights, motors, radios and so on.

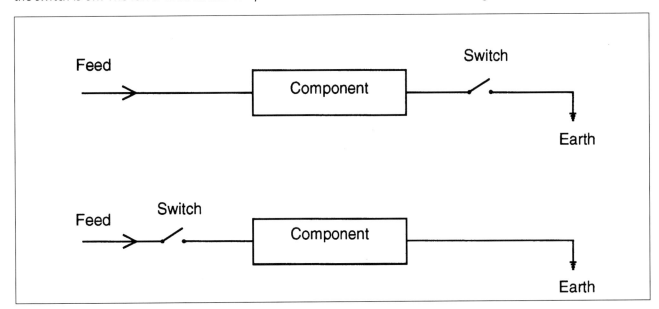

amount of resistance which is why you get voltage drop on a long cable. A twisted wire joint starts off with a low resistance when it's new but the resistance soon increases if the strands of copper wire tarnish, because the tarnish is a very poor conductor. Much the same applies to crimp-on terminals if they're not made with a proper heavy-duty crimping tool. Similarly, rust is a rotten conductor so, if you've got an earth return cable going to a bolt on the chassis, and it gets rusty, the resistance goes up, sometimes to the point where it becomes almost a non-conductor (the earthing strap of a battery is a prime example). A properly soldered joint is a very good conductor, but a badly soldered joint, sometimes called a 'dry' joint is a poor conductor.

But I'm getting ahead of myself just a little because I mentioned voltage drop without explaining the difference between voltage and current. It's easy enough to distinguish them. **Voltage is the force which pushes the**

Get yourself a few decent quality screwdrivers. They're much nicer to use than cheap ones and they'll last a long time without the points twisting or breaking and mauling the screw heads.

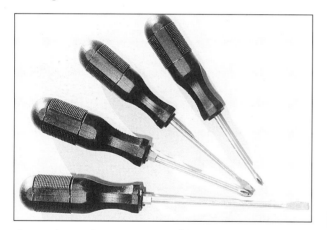

As an alternative to separate drivers, get a handle, either plain or ratchet, with a set of different sized bits. Once again, you can get cheap ones, but the better ones last.

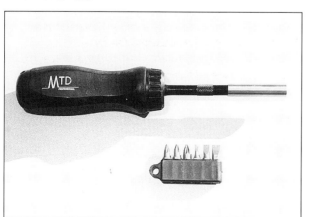

electricity along a conductor, so you get a voltage drop when you get a resistance in a circuit. Naturally enough, voltage is measured in volts, named after the Italian physicist Count Alessandro Volta. **Current is the amount of electricity which flows along the conductor**, so the less resistance you have the easier the current flows. Current is measured in amps, short for amperes and named after the French scientist Andre Ampere. **Resistance is measured in ohms**, named after the German physicist Georg Simon Ohm who first came up with Ohm's Law relating voltage, current and resistance, which I'll come to later when I'm dealing with sizes of cable. All these people lived in the seventeen hundreds and it's not essential to know their names, but I thought you might like to appear knowledgeable next time you're chatting at the pub.

So what makes a circuit? The four essentials are a feed, a

Sets of small instrument screwdrivers in plastic cases vary in price - and quality - from about £1 to £4. They do the job, but the ends vary in temper, sometimes so soft that they bend and sometimes so hard that they break. They do a job but, in our experience, they don't last very long.

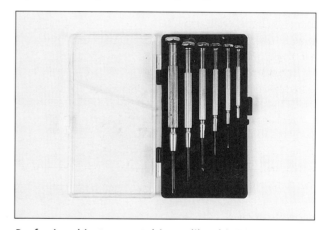

Professional instrument drivers, like this Facom set, cost around £20 but they're a pleasure to use and outlast a dozen cheap sets.

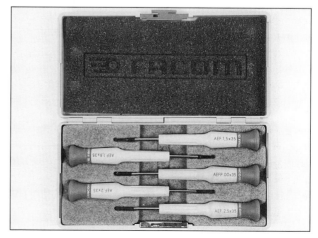

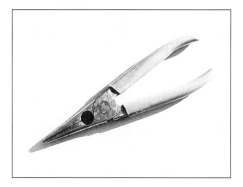

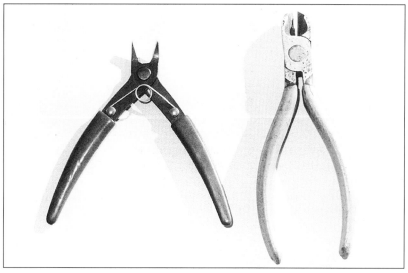

We find we use pointed nosed pliers on electrical work much more often than the flat-ended type. Good ones cost between £10 and £12 a pair but will last a lifetime. The cheap ones, often £1 to £1.50 on market stalls, are usually rubbish. The jaws often don't meet properly even when new, and soon splay out so that things ping out of them across the garage floor.

At least two pairs of side cutters are handy, one fairly heavy duty like the pair on the right and one pair for lighter work. The fine-pointed pair with the hairpin spring are very useful for delicate work on things like dash printed circuit boards.

switch, a component and a return. Leaving aside the charging circuit for the moment, our battery is our electrical storage box so, if we keep our circle in mind, all the feeds have got to start from the battery and the returns go back to it. If you get a break in any part of the circuit, the electricity won't flow.

The essentials of a circuit don't have to be in the same order. The usual order, as in something like a simple sidelamp circuit, is **feed - switch - component** (in this case the light bulb) - **and return**. You can, however, get some circuits where the order is changed to **feed - component - switch - return**. This is sometimes very convenient in the type of system known as chassis return, or sometimes earth return, or single pole. The car's body or chassis is usually referred to as 'earth'. It's used on just about all production cars with metal bodies. In this system, one terminal of the battery is the feed terminal and the other, the return terminal, is connected directly to the car's body or chassis.

In this case, the feed - component - switch - return circuit is used on things like courtesy lights. A feed cable goes to the interior lamp and a cable goes from there down to a switch in the metal door pillar. The body of the switch bolts in direct contact with the metal door pillar which is in electrical contact with the return side of the battery. So, when you open the door and the switch closes, the current flows and the lamp lights.

It's important to know whether you've got this type of circuit or the more usual feed - switch - component - return type because on a circuit like a courtesy light the cable to the lamp is live all the time the battery is connected and, if the bulb is good, so is the cable from the lamp down to the switch. Start undoing things without disconnecting the battery and you get a shower of fireworks. You often get a

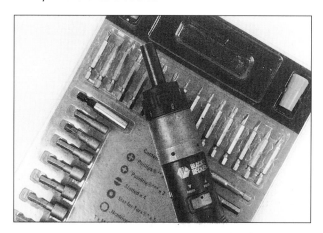

Above: A rechargeable electrical screwdriver with a complete set of bits may be a luxury but it's a nice luxury to have.

similar circuit on horn pushes. The big advantage is that you don't have to run two cables to the switch.

The other type of system is known as double pole, or sometimes insulated return. In this system, the battery and all the components are completely isolated from any metal part of the car and each component has a return cable going back to the battery. You get complete double-pole systems on things like petrol tankers because there's very much less chance of getting a spark. Then you get the sort of half and half system where part of it is single pole chassis return and part of it is double-pole. You used to get this on vintage cars with wood bodies because wood isn't a conductor. Then it died out on cars

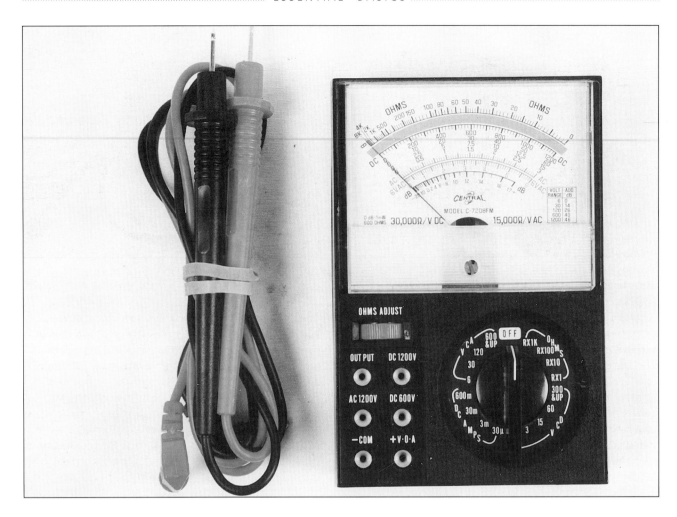

until people started making bodies out if glassfibre which is also a non-conductor.

The half and half system is quite common on kit cars where the heavy duty components like the starter and alternator are chassis return but components mounted on the glassfibre body are double-pole system with a return cable going back to the metal chassis. In a lot of cases, things can be simplified and one heavy-duty earth return cable to the chassis can serve several components.

You may have noticed that, 'till now, I haven't talked about positive and negative. Everybody knows that a battery has two terminals, one labelled positive, and usually coloured red, and the other labelled negative and usually coloured blue or black. It's normal to think of the electricity flowing from positive to negative, and that's the way I'll think about it in this book. Actually, the electron flow is from negative to positive.

The early electrical theorists got it the wrong way round but people thought about it like that for so many years that, when it was discovered that the electrons actually flowed the other way, the theorists decided to have two sorts of current flow, electron current which is negative to positive, and conventional current which is positive to negative. In practice, unless you're dealing with high-tech electronics, it

Analogue meters like this one are fairly delicate and need careful reading if you're after an accurate measurement. You also have to read the ohms scale backwards, which can sometimes be confusing.

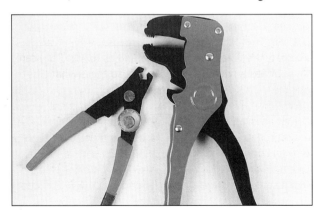

Above: Two types of insulation stripper. The smaller pair will do the job quite adequately but you sometimes need a sharp tug to get the insulation off the wire. The self-gripping type are bulkier but easy to use in confined places because all you need to do is pop the end of the wire in and squeeze the handles.

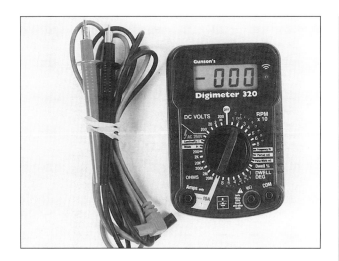

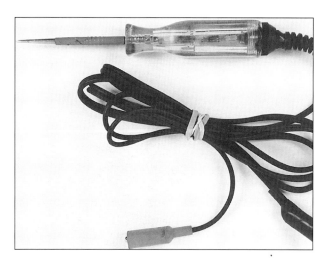

Mass produced electronic chips have brought the price of good digital meters like this Gunson's Digimeter 320 well within the DIY price range. They're robust, so accurate it hurts and, big advantage on this one, you can use it to read engine rpm and ignition dwell as well as volts, amps and ohms.

This is a feed and return prodder which will tell you if a terminal is a live feed or an earth return. You usually have to go to a professional auto electrical shop to buy them, and they cost from around £20 upwards.

doesn't matter a damn which way you think of it so, being a very conventional sort of bloke, I'm going to stay with conventional current and call the positive side of the battery the 'live' side.

All this is by way of being an aside, one of those 'incidentally' type of bits of knowledge, but it explains why, in the late fifties and early sixties, quite a few cars had systems where the positive side of the battery was connected to the chassis, the system known as positive-earth. It was supposed to help stop things like electronic corrosion in radiators and the like. Then when alternators took over from dynamos it was found to be much easier to go back to conventional current and connect the negative side of the battery to earth. You can polarise a dynamo to work either way, but not an alternator. Just about every kit car and its donor that I can think of has a negative earth system, so that's what I'll assume.

I mention this because, if you're poking around at autojumbles and the like, and you pick up something with a motor in it, like a wiper motor or an interior heater motor or even some relays, from the 1950s and early 1960s, be careful that it isn't from a positive earth system. If it is, it might still work on your negative earth system but motors might run backwards and relays might short out when you connect them up.

Right then, on to the tools you'll need. Actually, you won't need many so it pays to buy good quality. It's strange how some people will spend a lot of money buying a top quality socket set and then go and buy pliers and screwdrivers from a market stall. Get a good quality set of screwdrivers, both plain head and

cross-head, and keep them for electrical work. It's also very handy if you've got a set of smaller screwdrivers, sometimes called jeweller's or instrument drivers, for tackling the very small screws you sometimes come across on electrical stuff. Here again, get a good quality set. You can buy cheap and cheerful (more accurately described as cheap and nasty) sets in a small plastic box from DIY stores for about £1.99, or even for a quid on some market stalls, but they're just as nasty as they are cheap. They aren't made from good quality steel and they're not hardened and tempered properly so when you put a bit of force behind them either the tip bends or it breaks off, and probably ruins the screw as well. A top quality set of instrument screwdrivers will set you back anything from £15 to £20 but, if you treat them properly, you can pass them on to your grandchildren.

Much the same goes for pliers and side cutters. You can also buy these on market stalls for a pound or so but, when you look closely at them you find the jaws of the pliers aren't ground equally and the cutting edges of the side cutters often don't meet accurately. Hold them up to the light and check if you disbelieve me. Even if they look OK, the steel is such rotten quality that, with long pointed-nosed pliers, the ends of the jaws soon start to gape at the tip so small items go pinging off across the garage and, with any sort of pliers, the joint soon works loose so the jaws don't meet squarely.

You'll also need some very small spanners, and a set of very small sockets can also be a boon, if not a necessity, when it comes to stripping down components like starters, alternators and wiper motors. Fortunately, cheap and nasty small spanners are less plentiful in DIY shops and on market stalls than their bigger brothers. You usually have to get them from a proper tool shop where they stock good quality ones.

The same doesn't go for small socket sets. These abound in DIY shops and accessory shops, usually in cheap plastic packs. They're cheap, and they're rubbish. The sockets seldom fit the nuts properly, so they round them off, the adaptors from 3/8 inch drive down to 1/4 inch drive can snap off like carrots and the least said about the ratchets the better. About the only useful bit is the handle that looks like a screwdriver but with a 1/4 inch end to it, and even then the little ball that's supposed to stop the socket falling off doesn't do its job very well.

I know I've carried on a bit about the shortcomings of cheap tools, but some of them look so attractive nowadays and carry labels like 'Craftsman', or even sometimes 'Professional', that don't mean a thing. I've seen an awful lot of frustration and damaged components among home car builders caused by cheap tools. Stay with well-known top brands like Facom, Britool or the Sykes-Pickavant professional range and you won't go far wrong. They're a pleasure to use and, in the rare event of a tool not being up to scratch, the makers will change it. If you've got an electric screwdriver you can get small nut spinners to fit it from people like Bosch and Black & Decker. They're usually decent quality and very handy.

You'll need a pair of insulation strippers. Yes, we've seen some so-called 'professional' auto electricians strip insulation with a penknife against their thumb but it's a silly

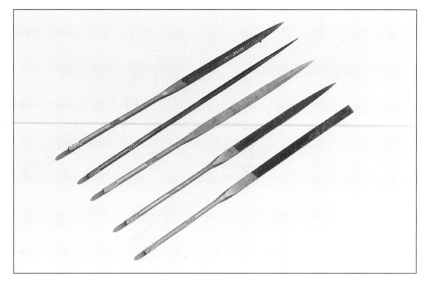

A set of small needle files is invaluable for cleaning up terminals and the like. For this work, even a cheap market stall set will give good service.

thing to do. Quite apart from the danger of cutting your thumb, there's a very good chance of cutting into one or more of the many strands inside the cable. This weakens it so it's likely to break off, and the cut strands have a habit of working loose and shorting out. Much the same objections, except that you won't cut your thumb, apply to using a pair of side cutters to strip insulation.

A little better than side cutters, but still not the best and easiest tool to use for the job, is the stripping tool looking like a pair of pliers which you can get in an accessory shop or which sometimes comes in a pack with some terminal connectors. It's better than plain side cutters because there is either an adjusting wheel or a series of vee cuts along the blade so you can choose one which will, with luck, cut the insulation and not the strands of the cable. Sometimes, the same tool purports to be ideal for crimping on terminal connectors, but it isn't. We'll come to that in a moment.

Better than these side-cutting strippers are the sort which the Post Office used to issue to its fitters. They look like an old-fashioned pair of pincers but the jaws overlap and have a pair of sharpened vee-shaped nicks in them. There's a side screw for adjusting the vee gap so they're suitable for just about any size of medium-duty cable. You see them sometimes at autojumbles on stalls which sell secondhand and ex-Government tools and, like all ex-GPO stuff, they're good quality, but they aren't as easy to use in confined spaces as the self-gripping type

This is the type of butane gas soldering iron we favour. You can pay upwards of £80 for a professional one but we've found that this £20 one from Tandy is quite robust and does a a good job.

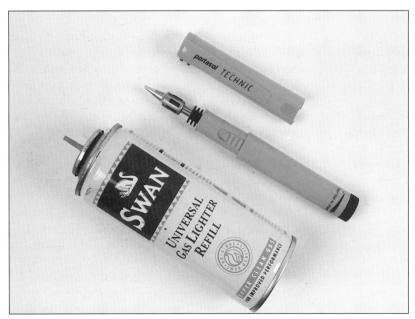

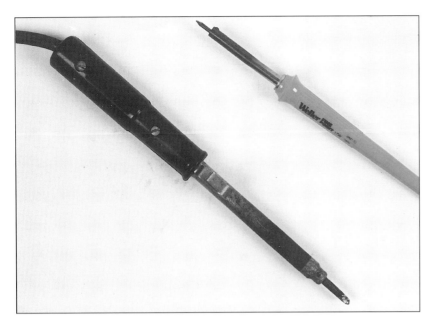

If you prefer an electric soldering iron, get a good quality one. The cheap ones soon burn out and it's often difficult to get replacement bits.

which we favour.

If you've ever tried to strip the insulation off the end of a cable deep down inside the bonnet or up under the dash you'll know that any type of insulation stripper where you have to pull to get the insulation off can be a damn nuisance. Either you can't get your elbows in a position to exert any force, or the insulation comes off suddenly and you're cursing a set of cut and bruised knuckles.

This is where the self-gripping type of insulation stripper scores. You just pop the end of the cable in, squeeze the handles and the end of the insulation comes off like a dream. No cut strands of wire and no damaged knuckles. As with most tools, there are cheap cantilever insulation strippers and expensive ones. The only way they can be cheapened is by lowering the quality so they don't last so long. Once again, go for a good pair and they'll last a lifetime.

I must admit that I'm not over-fond of crimped-on terminal connectors unless they were crimped on by the factory or by the loom maker with professional machinery. The sort of crimping tool that comes with a box of connectors from an accessory shop doesn't, in my opinion, do a particularly good job. I'm prepared for people to write in and say that that they've had a hundred per cent success with them, but I've seen plenty of home-crimped connectors where either the cable has pulled out or over-enthusiastic crimping has cut through the sleeve of the connector. I know they're convenient but I very much prefer a soldered join. If you really want to use crimping then at least get yourself a professional crimping tool from an electrical suppliers. They're expensive, but they do a good

job and you won't have cables pulling out. You'll also need a hydrometer for checking the condition of your battery, but I'll deal with that in the next chapter.

Earlier on I mentioned a meter, and the sort you want is a multimeter which will read volts, amps and ohms. In American catalogues, Americans often being quite down to earth, they're called VOA meters (Volts, Ohms, Amps).

There are two basic types of multimeter, the older analogue meter, the sort with a needle pointer, and the more modern digital meter which has a read-out panel like a calculator. For almost everything, the digital meter is superior. It's got an electronic chip inside it which makes it very accurate even though fine accuracy isn't essential in car wiring. After all, it doesn't really matter whether you've got 12.687 volts or 12.789 volts at a car component, it'll still work.

The big advantage of digital meters is that they're easy to read and there's practically no chance of making a mistake like there is when you're trying to distinguish between the eight or ten scales on an analogue meter in dim light. They are also much more robust. If you drop an analogue meter, even quite gently, the chances are you'll damage the pointer's bearings. I'm not saying that a digital meter can be bounced with impunity but at least it will come up smiling after a gentle knock. Digital meters also have the advantage that it's easy to incorporate a couple of extra, very useful, settings. These are continuity and diode test. Don't worry if the one you choose hasn't got a diode test labelled, you can use the continuity test to check diodes in alternators and, if you're going exotic, you can check some of the electrics on fuel-injected turbo engines like the Ford RS Turbo.

There's only one instance on car electrics that I can think of where an analogue meter is superior and that's for checking the smoothness of increasing resistance on throttle body switches and air flow sensor plates on some fuel injection systems. You can still do this with a digital meter, but it isn't so easy to read the smooth increase. On balance, and heavily weighted balance at that, I'd recommend a digital meter.

As for other things, you get what you pay for or, more accurately, you don't get what you don't pay for. However, as with most electronics, modern mass production of electronic chips in the Far East has brought prices tumbling. A lower priced digital meter is likely to be just as accurate as a higher priced one. What is sacrificed is robustness, quality of the casing, the rotary switch and printed circuit board and the quality control of manufacture. We wouldn't go for the cheapest, but there's no need to pay for the sort of meter an electronics engineer would buy. A mid-price digital meter like Gunson's Digimeter won't cost an arm and a leg and, with average care, will last a long time.

I could go through the procedures for using a meter but you'd probably forget half of them if I handed them to you in a big chunk, so I'll cover using the meter whenever it's appropriate to a particular job.

Allied to a meter, but doing just one specific job without measuring anything, is the type of prodder which will distinguish between a positive feed cable and an earth return cable. You connect its power leads to the car battery and then touch the end of the prodder against a terminal when the circuit is switched on. If it is the live feed terminal a lamp in the handle glows red, if it is an earth return terminal the lamp in the handle glows green. Like most tools, you can get cheap ones and more expensive ones. The cheap ones do the job but need to be handled with care if they are to last whereas the more expensive ones are made to put up with hard professional use.

For cleaning up terminals and such like, a few small files which you keep for electrical work come in very handy. Because they're doing only light duty, even the cheap ones are quite adequate for this work, and a set of needle files in a plastic case can be bought very cheaply in most tool shops and on autojumble stalls.

Having said that I prefer soldered joints to crimped joints, I ought to say a few words about soldering irons. The type I favour for car wiring is the butane gas type which you can refill from a pressurised can of butane lighter fuel. As always, you can pay a lot for a professional one - the Weller one sets you back anything from £80 upwards depending where you buy it - but this can be classed as a bit of a luxury for home kit car wiring. You can, however, buy one in Tandy and other toolshops at around £20 which, if you look after it, is robust enough to last a long time. This type of iron has two big advantages. The first is that you don't have to have a cable trailing from it which makes it easier to use in somewhat confined places like under the dash. The second is that it blows out enough heat just below the soldering tip to shrink a length of heat-shrink cable insulation, an invaluable aid to wiring.

However, if you feel happier with an electric iron and don't mind having the cable hanging on the end, by all means go for one. You can get good quality ones, like a Weller, quite cheaply and, if you buy a well-known name, you can be sure of getting replacement bits when you need them. Don't underestimate this advantage, the bits do burn away and need cleaning frequently when you're doing a lot of soldering, and they don't last for ever. You can buy rechargeable electric soldering irons but my experience of them hasn't been too happy. Unless you pay a lot of money for them, the battery doesn't last very long between charges and you tend to find that soldering a join begins to take longer and longer, 'till eventually the solder doesn't melt properly and then you wonder how many joins back you've got to check to make sure you haven't got any high resistance 'dry' joins.

You can also get small electrical soldering irons that run on 12 volts and have either two clips on the end of the cable to connect to the battery or sometimes a plug to fit in the car's cigarette lighter. They're OK for occasional very light jobs, but for car building I haven't found them powerful enough to do the job on anything but the lightest of cables. They're intended more for model makers.

Chapter 2

BATTERY CARE

Choosing and caring for your battery, possibly the
most neglected component on the car.

TO MANY OF US, A BATTERY'S JUST A BOX. THERE'S
nothing mechanical to go wrong, nothing to lubricate, so it
sits under the bonnet or under the seat or in the boot,
depending on the car's design and, because it's so reliable,
it's largely forgotten till one day it gets tired and the car
won't start.

That's not a very kind way to treat such a hard working
and reliable friend which, like a faithful dog, doesn't ask
much in return for a lifetime's service. And, like it says in the
adverts for a particular brand of dog food, you can Prolong
its Active Life with the right food and attention. But that's
enough comparisons, let's get down to brass tacks about
choosing and looking after the battery.

Lead-acid batteries haven't changed a lot in principle since
before the war. They still have a series of positive and
negative plates in each cell submerged in an electrolyte of
dilute sulphuric acid, but battery technology's advanced a lot
to make them smaller, lighter, more reliable and very much
longer lasting than they were even ten years ago. That's why
they get neglected more.

*If you're removing a battery from a car for any length
of time, cover the terminals with tape to avoid any
possibility of spanners etc shorting across the
terminals.*

*Old batteries can often have corrosion acid and grime
on the outer casing, so be careful where you leave
them. Here the cut-off side of an old oil can makes an
ideal tray.*

When a battery fails it's nearly always because the
chemical paste on the plates either dries up and gets a
coating of sulphate because you've let the electrolyte level
get too low, or the paste gradually falls off the plates
because of vibration and collects at the bottom of the cell
where it shorts out the positive and negative plates. This
internal shorting used to be quite common
on older batteries but it seldom happens
nowadays because on modern batteries the
plates are enclosed in porous plastic
envelopes which allow the electrolyte to get
through but stop the paste from falling off.
This means it's no longer necessary to leave a
big empty space at the bottom of the battery
case where the sediment can collect which is
one of the reasons why modern battery
casings are much less high than older
designs.

Batteries are also a lot lighter, partly
because the cases are now lightweight plastic
instead of thick heavy rubberised ebonite,
and partly because the design of the plates
and the chemicals used in the paste are much
more efficient than they used to be.

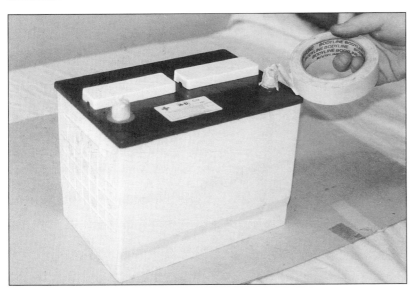

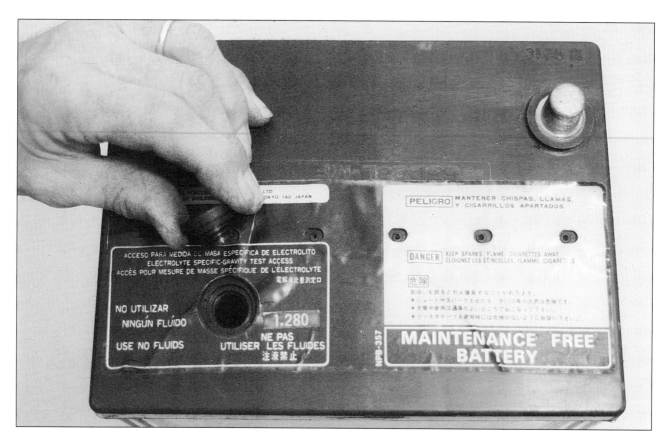

Above: We know it says 'Use no fluids' on this maintenance free battery but it has a translucent side casing and, when we found the electrolyte level low, we topped it up with de-ionised water and, so far, it's given a further 11 months service with no ill effects.

Below: Older batteries used to be rated in ampere-hours but now, like this one, they're rated in reserve capacity. If your donor car is an older one, and the manual rates the battery in ampere-hours, most battery shops will have a catalogue giving the correct newer rating for your car.

So, if modern batteries are so much better, why do they fail at all? Sometimes, they fail because the owner has chosen the wrong size battery for the system or, more usually, because the battery doesn't get enough work to do and possibly hasn't been given any attention from day one. Battery makers themselves are partly to blame for this because they stress either 'Low Maintenance' or even 'Maintenance Free' in their sales blurb. They as good as tell you to fit it and forget it but, if you do, you'll probably get about three to four years' life from it whereas with a little care and attention there's no real reason why a good quality modern battery shouldn't last eight or nine years.

I'll come to battery maintenance in a moment but first I want to talk about choosing a battery. I said that batteries sometimes fail because they're the wrong size and you might think that's because they're too small but, quite often, the reverse is the reason. If you fit a battery that's a little too small for the system it has to work harder, but it doesn't mind that. Batteries thrive on hard work but sometimes die from boredom. The big drawback of a small battery is that it may not have enough reserve capacity. It gets very sluggish on a cold morning because batteries are a bit like us, they're not at their best when they're feeling the cold. If the car doesn't start after a couple of attempts, a small battery might cry enough for the moment and need a rest before it's able to try again. By and large, though, it won't come to a lot of harm.

Conversely, if you fit a battery that's much larger than the system really needs, and you haven't got an alternator with enough output to keep it fully charged it's going to stay about half-charged for most of its life. It will probably still have enough reserve capacity to spin the engine over in a lively enough fashion, but batteries don't like being half charged and they don't like not having to work very hard. They're happiest in a constant cycle of charge and discharge, otherwise the chemicals in the plates gradually harden and eventually won't take a full charge.

Batteries used to be rated in ampere-hours, the time it

Right: There's only one certain way to check if a battery's in good condition and that's to use a hydrometer to take a specific gravity reading on each cell. It's one of the disadvantages of some maintenance free batteries that you can't check each cell, only the overall specific gravity.

Below: A home battery charger which tapers off the charging current as the battery becomes more fully charged will keep your battery in good condition while you're not using it as well as giving it an occasional top-up.

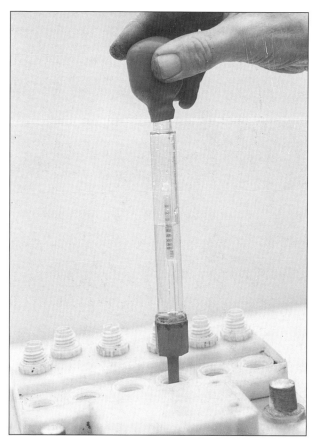

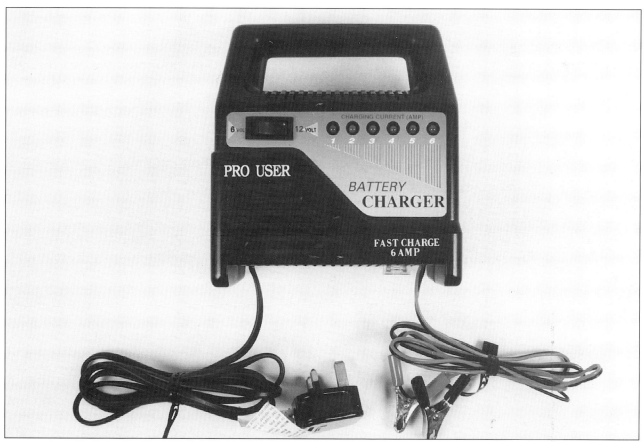

took for the battery to go from fully charged to fully discharged multiplied by the discharge current. If you're building a car using a fairly oldish design of donor you'll probably find the size of battery is quoted in ampere-hours in the donor's manual. Some battery makers still rate batteries in ampere-hours for their own internal factory purposes but, on the battery itself, you'll find a newer system in use. This rates the battery using a calculation of reserve capacity and the time taken for the voltage to drop to a certain level under heavy discharge. The new system isn't directly related to the old ampere-hour system but most battery makers' catalogues list the right size of battery for

Above: Make sure the terminals at the battery are clean and tight. Below: To stop corrosion and green crystals, coat the terminals with vaseline.

older cars as well as current models so you should be able to find your donor car listed.

You might want to uprate your alternator if you load up the car with extra electrics like driving and fog lights and bags of watts of stereo, so keep any later requirements like this in mind when you're choosing the battery. If you're going to uprate to a bigger alternator, look up the size of battery for the standard car which uses this larger alternator and fit that one rather than the smaller battery that may have been intended for the electrical demands of something like a 1100 Escort.

Very few batteries get fully charged for long when they're

in use on the car, particularly in winter. A survey by a battery manufacturer showed that, on average, batteries are seldom charged to much more than 70 per cent of their rated capacity in winter, sometimes even less if the car is used only on short journeys. When the maker specified the size of battery for your donor car, he looked at volt-amp graphs supplied by the battery maker. These graphs show up another peculiarity of lead acid batteries. A fully-charged battery which is asked to deliver a current of, say, 8 amps, might well give this at 12 volts. Ask it to deliver 80 or more amps for the starter, and the voltage could well drop to as low as 8.5 to 9 volts in a few seconds, depending on the battery capacity.

This is why you get ballast resistors in some coil ignition circuits. The coil is made to run at around 9 volts and, when the battery's delivering 12 volts, there's a ballast resistor to cut this down for normal running. When you turn the key to start the engine, the battery voltage may drop to about 9 volts, so the same action by-passes the ballast resistor and lets full battery voltage to the coil to give a good spark.

For reliable starting in winter, the battery should be able to crank the engine at 100 rpm, so the car maker consulted the volt-amp graphs and the temperature graphs, and picked a battery which would crank the engine at 100 rpm in freezing conditions even though it was only 70 per cent charged.

What about 'cheap' batteries compared with those having a well-known brand name? In accessory shops you can find own-brand batteries that look very similar to batteries with a nationally known name, but quite often at nearly half the price. These are quite reputable batteries and are in much the same category as own-brand goods on the shelves of a supermarket in that they're made under large-order contracts for battery distributors and wholesalers by the major battery manufacturers but without the manufacturer's name on them.

They may not use the latest top-of-the-range technology, but they're perfectly good batteries even though they're built down to price and probably won't have as many plates in each cell as top-brand batteries. Generally speaking, if a battery's got a fewer number of thick plates in each cell instead of a larger number of thin ones, it can be made more cheaply but its volt-amp graph won't be the same. If the engine doesn't want to start one morning you'll probably find that the cut-price battery runs out of volts a little more quickly than a top-brand one and won't crank a cold engine over for as long a time. These cut-price batteries are sold in bulk to distributors and wholesalers without a maker's guarantee so, even if you find out who made it, they won't be interested if it fails. You have to take it up with the shop where you bought it, but the shop's guarantee is usually pretty good. It will probably cover you for three years instead of the normal five years on a top-brand battery or even, in some cases, a lifetime guarantee to the first purchaser.

Batteries don't like long periods of standing about doing nothing, especially if they're only partly charged. They get bored and the chemicals inside start coating the plates with lead sulphate which steadily reduces the battery's capacity and makes it more difficult to charge. Batteries last longest if they're constantly charged and discharged so, when you buy a new battery halfway during the kit car build, swap it over from time to time with the battery on your everyday car if it's suitable. If you can't do this for any reason, discharge the battery regularly, at least once a fortnight, by connecting a headlamp bulb across the terminals. You can use it as a lead light, or a light over the bench, in the garage. Then, when the bulb gets dim, recharge the battery.

Trickle charging at a steady 2 or 3 amps is undoubtedly the best way to charge a battery, but most home battery chargers have a device in them which sees the voltage of the battery while it's being charged. When the battery's fully discharged the charger will probably put in around 6 to 7 amps but will taper this down as the battery becomes more fully charged, eventually dropping down to about half an amp or so. This is a good thing, because it means that you can leave the battery on charge and almost forget it.

Before you take it off charge, make sure it is actually fully charged. Putting a voltmeter across the terminals will give you an idea, but it isn't the most accurate way, and it won't tell, on an older battery, if one or more of the cells is starting to get a shade weak. This is where you need an essential piece of kit that won't cost you very much - a battery hydrometer.

These are quite simple devices, basically a glass, or nowadays plastic, tube with a weighted float inside and a rubber bulb at the top so you can poke the end in each cell in turn and draw off some of the electrolyte. The specific gravity of the electrolyte changes depending on the state of charge of the battery, the more fully charged it is, the higher the specific gravity so the float will float higher.

The float has a scale on it and, on some cheap hydrometers you get just three coloured bands, usually labelled something like full, half and low. They will give you a reasonable idea of the battery's state of charge but the float doesn't have to be weighted so accurately as one which has figures on it. I always prefer to work with figures and, with a fully-charged battery, the hydrometer should read between 1.27 and 1.29 at each cell. A reading between 1.23 and 1.25 indicates about 70 per cent charged, and if it's as low as 1.11 to 1.13, the cell is practically flat.

Strictly speaking, hydrometer reading should be taken with the electrolyte at 15 degrees C (60 degrees F), so they

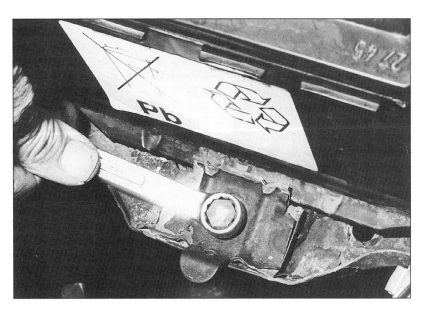

Clamp the battery down firmly. A loose battery is an MOT failure as it could tip and spill acid in the event of an accident.

won't be a truly accurate guide if the battery's still hot after a boost charge or freezing cold on a winter morning. If you're a real fusspot for accuracy, check the temperature of the electrolyte and use the temperature conversion table which ought to come with the hydrometer. However, most people don't bother about this degree of accuracy, and I must admit I don't either.

The most useful aspect of using a hydrometer is to check that all the cells are in roughly the same condition, either charged or not. If, after charging, five of the six cells are fully up and one is only half charged it means that the odd cell is starting to break down. The battery might last a little while longer, but it will fail quite quickly.

Some garages offer an emergency boost charge service which charges the battery quickly, in an hour or less, at a much higher current, usually up to about 70 per cent fully charged. Some more expensive home chargers can do the same. Using a boost charge once or twice in a battery's life probably won't harm it, unless it's already on the way out, but regular use of a boost charger will. Boost charging heats up a battery, and the temperature should not be allowed to rise above about 43 degrees C (110 degrees F). The better boost chargers have a temperature probe which sits in one of the middle cells and which cuts down the current as the temperature rises. In any case, boost charging ought not to be carried out for more than an hour, and should be stopped at once if the battery starts gassing vigorously.

That brings us to another, most important, point about charging a battery. When a battery's being charged it gives off gases, both hydrogen and oxygen. If you've seen the old newsreel film about the fire on the airship Hindenburg you'll realise how quickly a spark can turn hydrogen gas into a

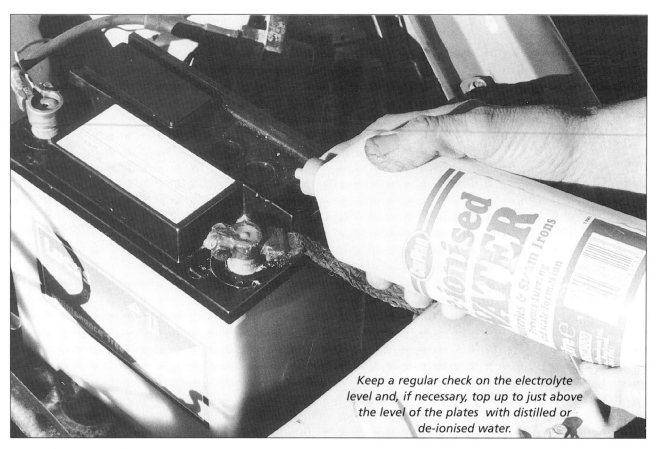

Keep a regular check on the electrolyte level and, if necessary, top up to just above the level of the plates with distilled or de-ionised water.

Not all kit cars will have dedicated battery location positions. However, this old Dutton has a purpose made battery spot. Wherever you place the battery, make sure it is well secured.

sheet of flame. Mix it with oxygen and you can get an explosive mixture which could even blow the battery casing apart. It doesn't take a lot to spark it off, the tiny spark when you connect or disconnect a clip from the terminal of the battery is enough, so always remember these golden rules:

> **ALWAYS** take the vent cover or vent plugs off a battery before you charge it.
> **NEVER** connect or disconnect the clips of the charging leads while the charger is switched on.
> **NEVER** do any welding or have any sort of naked flame in the garage while a battery's on charge.
> **NEVER** light a cigarette anywhere near a battery which is on charge.

I once saw the results of a battery exploding while a mechanic was working near it and, even though he was fortunate and not seriously injured, it wasn't pleasant.

Apart from checking the specific gravity about once every couple of months and giving the battery a charge if necessary, there are two other points about battery maintenance. The first is topping up the electrolyte. When a battery is being charged, either by a charger or by the alternator, some of the electrolyte comes off as gas, and it also looses some by evaporation. But, unless you spill some out of the battery, it doesn't loose any acid. The gases are hydrogen and oxygen, the constituents of water, and only water is lost by evaporation.

In some accessory shops you see bottles of 'Battery Topping-up Liquid' which is a very dilute sulphuric acid. Forget it. The only time you need to add acid to a battery is

if you've been clumsy enough to knock it over and spill some. Then you should top it up again with sulphuric acid of the correct dilution which you can buy from a battery shop.

For all other topping up use only distilled water or the much cheaper de-ionised water. Ordinary tap water contains all sorts of purifying chemicals which can shorten the life of a battery. Neither boiling nor putting it through one of those proprietary filters for drinking will take them all out. I have seen it advocated that you can use melted ice or frost from inside a fridge or freezer, but it's a very poor second best and probably not very pure water. When you top up, use a plastic or glass container, not a metal one as even distilled water can take metal salts over with it and these won't do your battery any good at all. You should top up, till the electrolyte is just above the top of the plates, and wipe the top of the battery to mop up any water you've spilt. I usually use throw-away kitchen roll paper for this, then there's no danger of rags with acid or other nasties being used on paintwork.

The other point about battery maintenance is to check that the terminal clamps are clean and tight. If they start growing pretty green and white crystals round them, remember what I said in Chapter 1 about high resistance joints. Clean the crystals off by pouring a kettle of hot water over them, it's by far the best and easiest way. Then dry them, clean them up and coat them with Vaseline or commercial petroleum jelly, not ordinary car grease. While you're about it, check that the connection of the battery earthing strap to the chassis is clean and tight. Quite a lot of 'failing' batteries and 'failing' alternators have been cured by cleaning and tightening the battery connections.

Chapter 3

USING A SOLDERING IRON

If you want to be certain about your terminals, connectors and
wiring junctions, the only safe way is to solder them.

OVER THE YEARS I'VE SEEN SOME PRETTY AWFUL EXAMPLES
of wiring and making connections on donor cars and, let's
face it, on some kit cars where the old loom's been adapted.
The electrical system on a car is enough of an Achilles' heel
without helping unreliability on its way with poor connections
and, as I said earlier, the best and most sure way is to solder.

Soldering a connection, or making a T-junction into a cable,
is so simple when you go about it the right way yet some
people shy away from it or, when they try it, make a bodge
of it. Let's look at the proper way to go about it.

The two big enemies of good soldering are grease and
tarnish so make sure that everything is clean and bright.
Sometimes you find that, when you strip the insulation, old

*Here's a couple of examples of connections we're not
keen on. The clip-together type on the left is fine if
you can be certain that no moisture is ever going to
get near it but, once it gets condensation inside, the
connections develop a high resistance. We've proved
this several times when we've been trouble-shooting
by putting an ohm-meter across old clip-together
connections. The crimped-on terminal on the right was
put on with a DIY crimping tool which came together
with a box of terminals as an 'auto-electrician's
terminal set'. It didn't crimp very tightly, nor was it
waterproof so, once again, condensation had got
inside and made a high-resistance join.*

wire has tarnished inside and doesn't want to take the solder.
The best plan is to use new wire but if for any reason, such as
the wire being part of an existing loom, this is unpractical,
then you must clean all the strands with fine glasspaper
followed by a wipe with switch cleaner before you start.

There's also the process known as tinning, coating the end
of the wire and the end of the terminal with solder before
you bring them together. You don't need to do this on a T-
junction but it's essential when you're soldering a terminal on
the end of a cable. You should also tin the end of a new
soldering iron bit before you use it. On electrical work, never
use a separate flux. I would advise against using even the
paste fluxes which are labelled non-corrosive and certainly
never use liquid flux of the type known as Baker's fluid. It's an
excellent flux but it's very corrosive and unless you scrub
things off with hot water and soda afterwards – which is
quite impractical on electrical work – it will turn the cables
and terminals green and horrible in a week or so. Wire solder

*This is the old type of rubber-sleeved push-in bullet
connector which used to be very popular. You can still
get plastic-sleeved connectors like this today, but we
don't like them very much. They're useful, but they
aren't water proof and, yet again, condensation
makes a high resistance. If you need to make
detachable connections, have a look at the ones on
modern Fords, they're far superior.*

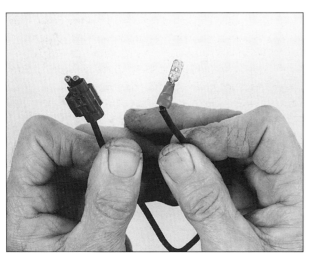

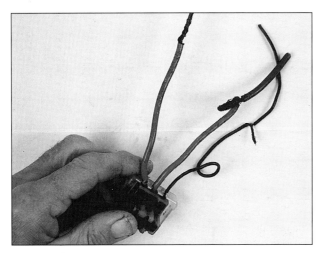

Above: Look at this bunch of horrors. This was the main cable from the alternator on a donor car and, not only were the joins just twisted together, they were 'insulated' with masking tape. No wonder the thing wasn't charging properly. YUK! Below: Three simple steps in making an extension join. Step one, you strip the ends of the insulation, slip a piece of heat-shrink tubing on and twist the wire ends together.

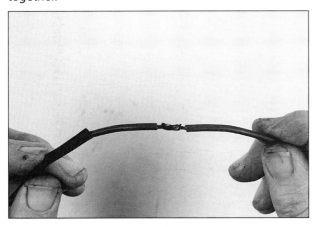

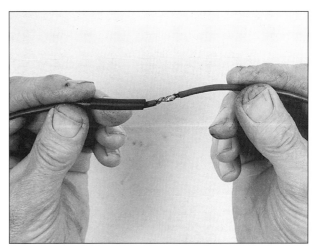

Above: Step two, you run solder in to the twisted join. Below: Step three, bring the heat-shrink tubing over the join and shrink it down to make the job perfectly insulated and waterproof.

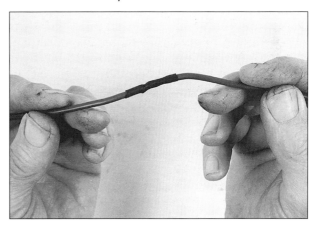

made for electrical work contains its own non-corrosive flux and you don't need to add anything else.

Tinning, like all soldering, is very simple once you recognise one golden rule. Don't melt the solder on to the tip of the iron and then transfer it to the join. Heat the end of the wire, or the terminal, with the soldering iron and keep touching it with the end of the wire solder till the solder melts and flows over it. That way you make sure the wire or the terminal is hot enough to make the solder take properly. Do it any other way and the solder just blobs on the outside like Plasticine and you get a high-resistance joint, usually known as a 'dry' joint.

The next point is stripping insulation. Again it's a simple job but we've seen plenty of connections where the stripping has cut into one or more of the strands of wire. This weakens the join so the wire's likely to break off. As I mentioned in an earlier chapter, use a proper insulation stripper and set it for the thickness of cable you're using.

Right, let's go through making a soldered T-join into a cable. First use your stripper to cut the insulation back in the cable to which you want to join another one, and then strip the insulation off the end of the cable you're joining to it. Twist the exposed end round the wire of the first cable – this is one case where you don't do any tinning first – then hold the soldering iron bit against the wires under the join and keep touching the end of the solder to the wires until it flows and makes a perfect, bright join. Hold things still for a moment or two to let the solder set after you take the soldering iron away, and the job's almost done.

I say almost because you've still got to insulate it and make it waterproof. Wherever I can I like to use heat-shrink tubing for this job but it isn't practical on a T-join into a loom because you can't slip the tubing on to the cable, so the best thing to use is self-amalgamating tape. This, if you haven't come across it before, is insulating tape that has a silicon paper on one side of it otherwise you'd never get it to unroll. You cut a length off the roll, peel off the silicon paper and wrap the tape round the join, pressing it tightly together. In an hour or two the tape will have amalgamated, or fused together, so it never comes undone and makes the join completely waterproof. As well as being used by electricians, self-amalgamating tape is used by plumbers so, if you can't find it in your local car accessory shop try either an electrical supplies shop or a plumber's supply shop. My local ironmonger sells it.

Now I'll run through soldering terminal on to the end of a cable. Once again strip the insulation off the end of the cable but don't make the mistake of stripping off too much, half an inch is quite enough. Hold the bit of your iron against the underneath of the exposed wire and touch your solder to the top until it flows and joins all the strands together. Now slip a short length of heat-shrink tubing on to the end of the cable before you solder the terminal on.

Next, tin the end of the terminal in a similar way. Then bring the two together and hold the iron bit under the terminal 'till the solder on the terminal and wire both melt and fuse together to give you a perfect join with zero resistance. You'll notice in the illustration that I'm holding the cable and the terminal in a modeller's clamp. You can buy these for a few pounds in model shops or, sometimes, at autojumbles, and they make the job simple as well as avoiding burnt fingers.

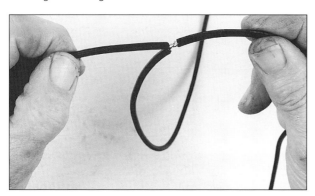

Above: Making a T-join into a loom is very similar to making an extension join. First, you strip back the insulation and twist the wires together. Below: Then you run solder into the twisted join to make it permanent.

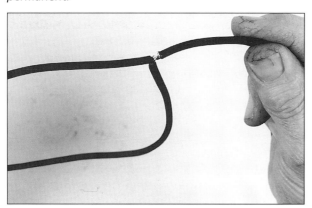

Once the join's cooled down, slide the heat-shrink tubing up over the join and heat it 'till it shrinks and makes everything neat and waterproof. If you're using a butane gas iron you can use the heat from the side of it to shrink the tubing. That's one of the reasons why I like using a butane iron. But, if you really prefer an electrical iron, use a pencil-type butane torch on it's lowest setting to shrink the tubing. It doesn't need a lot of heat, but something like a hair drier just isn't powerful or concentrated enough.

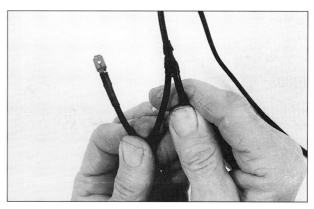

Above: Finally you insulate it with self-amalgamating tape. You'll see that, on this job, we also needed to put a connector on the end of the cable, which we'll run through next. Below: First we stripped and tinned the end of the cable. Note the handy modeller's clamp for holding the cable.

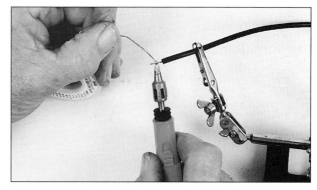

Below: When it was tinned, we snipped the end to the right length to fit inside the terminal.

If you need to extend a cable, you make an in-line join in exactly the same way as a T-join except that this time you can use heat-shrink tubing to insulate it.

And that's about it. Making soldered connections is such a simple job but it gives you perfect joins and peace of mind. Once you get the hang of it I'm sure you won't want to use crimped or clip-on joins ever again.

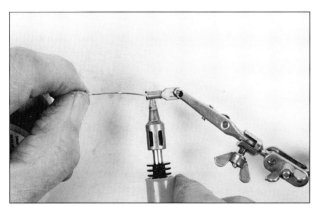

Above: Next job was to tin the inside of the terminal where the wire was going to sit. Below: Then we held the iron under the terminal to keep the solder molten while we pushed the tinned wire inside. After a second or two they fused together and the job was done apart from using heat-shrink tubing to insulate it.

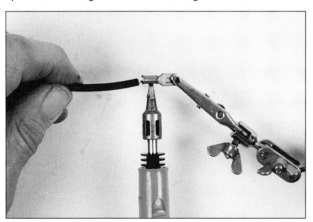

This is how we found the connections to the switch for a heated rear window that wasn't working properly. The connectors were poorly crimped on and 'insulated' with masking tape.

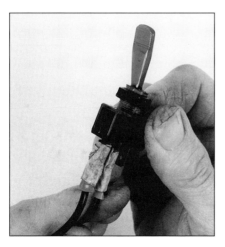

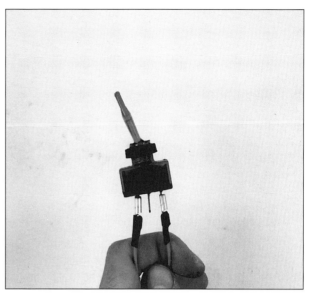

Above: This is the job done properly, with soldered connections and heat-shrink tubing. If we'd needed to insulate it further we'd have used self-amalgamating tape over the heat-shrink. Below: You might be puzzled by this type of multi-connector, often used on headlamps. The terminals inside the block corrode but there doesn't seem to be any way to get them out to renew them. The simple answer is to slip a narrow screwdriver down one side of the terminal to push back a small tag that holds the terminal in the block.

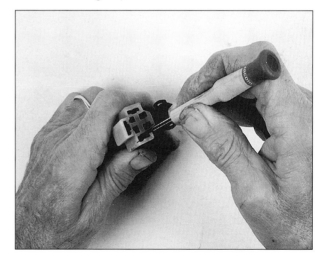

This is the tag you have to push back to get the terminal free. You can buy these tagged terminals at auto-electrical supply shops, such as Lucas agents. Solder them on in a similar way to any other terminal.

This is how NOT to strip insulation. You're likely to cut some of the wire strands as well as your thumb.

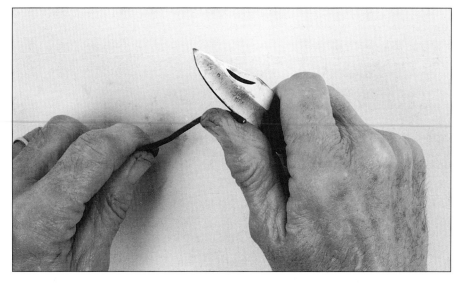

Below: This type of insulation stripper with a dial setting for different cable thickness is fine if you've got room to tug the insulation off the end of the cable.

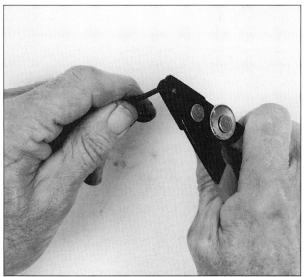

The easiest sort of stripper to use is the self-gripping type. Just squeeze the handles and insulation's off. It makes working in a confined space – like under the dash – much easier.

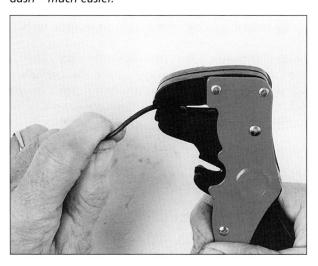

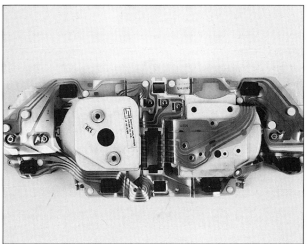

Unless you're very skilled at soldering don't try it on a printed circuit dash like this. It takes very little heat to lift the thin copper circuit runs away from the board. It does, however, pay to clean the connecting strips on a printed circuit with switch contact cleaner and a cotton bud.

Chapter 4

UNDERSTANDING WIRING DIAGRAMS

Baffled by masses of lines? Here's how to sort out

the spaghetti jungle.

BACK IN THE DIM AGES OF CAR ELECTRICS ONLY TWO colours of cable were used, red for live feeds and black for return to earth. As electrics increased in complexity, other colours were used for different circuits and, when the different colours ran out, two colours were used on some cables, a main body colour and a thin line of a different colour, usually called a tracer. Over the years there have been numerous attempts to arrive at a standard colour coding. There's a British Standard, a Lucas standard, a German DIN (Deutsch Industrie Norm) standard, an American SAE (Society of Automotive Engineers) standard and an ISO (International Standards Organisation) standard.

Unfortunately, they differ considerably and, even more unfortunately, some car makers ignore all the standards and go their own sweet way. Ford is notorious for this and sometimes even varies the colours used on different circuits for different models. There's yet more opportunity for confusion in that different wiring diagrams, sometimes even from the same car maker, use different abbreviations for the different colours. It's almost as if designers set out to confuse people, but here's a list, probably not complete, of the colour abbreviations I've found and you may come across.

Blue	B or Bl
Light Blue	Hgl
Black	Bk, S, Sw or N
Brown	Bn, or Br
Green	G, Gn or V
Light Green	Lgr
Red	R, Ro, Rd or Rt
Pink	Rs, Pi or S
Grey or Slate	S, Sl, G or Gr
Violet	V or Vi
Purple	Pu
Lilac	Li
White	W, Ws, Wh or Bc
Yellow	Y, Yw, Ge or J
Beige	Be
Orange	Or
Clear (transparent)	C
Maroon	M

Some of the differences, like V standing for green instead of violet, N for black and J for yellow come from the initials for verde, noir and jaune and are found on French diagrams like those for Renaults and Citroens. On some diagrams you may find all the letters as capitals, some a mixture and on others all as lower case. It isn't usual to come across violet, purple and lilac together on the same diagram though I did once find purple and violet on the same car, a Renault, where the purple was a really royal deep purple and the violet looked like a washed-out tinted blue.

All this shows how essential it is to get the wiring diagram for the donor car you're using, and don't assume just because it's a Cortina that the colours on a Mk II Cortina are the same as on a Mk IV or on a Sierra. For some circuits they aren't. Be very careful of close colours, particularly on thin lines of tracer colour. You might be able to distinguish easily between blue and violet in daylight but, in the light from a tungsten lead lamp, they can look very similar. You might also find that you've got slight colour blindness under artificial light between light green and grey or blue and purple. This slight colour blindness is more common than many people think and is seldom noticed in everyday life, so check a few cables against the wiring diagram just to be certain you can distinguish them when you're lying under the dash or grovelling deep down inside the car in a dim light.

With regard to what colours are used on what circuits, there is a sort of standard. Brown is usual as a main colour on live feeds to switches, blue and red are usual for feeds from switches to components (blue is often used for headlights), green is often used for feeds to fused components controlled by the ignition switch and white is sometimes used for the feeds to components which are not fused and are controlled by the ignition switch. All these colours may have added identifying tracers. Don't take these as gospel, though, because it ain't necessarily so.

On, then, to wiring diagrams, the masses of lines that can give you an eye ache and headache if you pore over them for too long trying to sort out what goes to where and whereabouts it is on the car or loom. There are several different types of wiring diagram, one being purely diagrammatic and often called the 'rail' type of diagram. A second method tries to get everything on one massive diagram so that you have to sort out for yourself which circuit is which. Then there is the third type that splits the electrics up into their basic circuit groups with a separate diagram for each group. I'll start by having a look at this third type of diagram, because once you get to understand this type the others become easier.

I've taken as an example part of the diagram of the starting and charging circuits for the Sierra. The parts we're most interested in here are the battery, alternator, starter motor and steering ignition switch, all of which are labelled. I've gone over the cables we'll be looking at and thickened them slightly to make them easier to follow. On the original diagram the cables are, of course, all the same thickness. Look at the bottom of the battery, the negative end, and you'll find a code C - 1301. Then, in the cable, comes the code 31 - SW, followed by C - 1002 and G - 1002.

The C - codes are connections and refer to the type of connector used. The 31 - SW in the cable means that it is cable no. 31 and it's black (SW). It goes to a connector C - 1002, and the G code means that it is an earth, or ground, point. Separate boxes on the diagram show the type of connector and the location of the earth point. In this case,

G - 1002 is given as 'Located near battery' and it's obviously the main battery earthing cable.

From the positive end of the battery we've got another connector type 1301 and two cables. One, cable number 30 which is RT, or red, goes to the starter motor or, more accurately as you can see, the starter motor solenoid and it's obviously the main heavy feed to the starter. The other cable starts with a fuse link wire and goes to a point coded S - 1001. The S codes stand for soldered joints and, again, a box elsewhere on the diagram tells us where they are. In this case, S - 1001 is also 'Located near battery'.

A word here about fuse link wires which Ford is quite fond of using. These look very similar to any other cable but, as their name implies, they are fuses and will 'blow', or melt, if the current goes above a certain figure. They're much more robust than ordinary fuses and will blow only if there's a prolonged dead short. So, for example, if you got a dead short under the dash or in the steering column loom, the normal fuses wouldn't blow because they are

This is the starting and charging circuit for a Sierra with some of the cables thickened so you can follow them from the text.

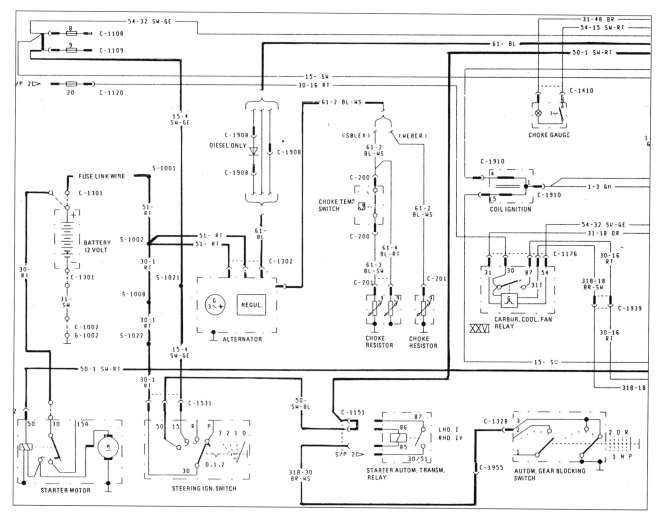

after the lighting and ignition switch, or upstream as some electricians call it. The fuse link wire would, however, melt and become open circuit to cut off all the supply from the battery before, we hope, the short heated things up enough to cause a fire.

After the soldered joint, the cable becomes number 51 and it's also RT, or red. It goes to another soldered joint S - 1002 which, the box on the diagram tells us, is 'Located near alternator'. From S - 1002, there are two cables labelled 51, both red, and both going to the alternator. The reason there are two is that, on a high output alternator (it can be up to 70 amps on a Sierra) using two cables means that each can be a smaller diameter than one thick heavy cable, and it's easier to fix connectors to the ends. Also from soldered join S - 1002 goes another red cable, number 30, which goes to S - 1008, located near the fuse box and then to S - 1022 which is located near the steering ignition switch.

Finally, it goes to the steering ignition switch through what seems to be a three-pin connector C - 1531 so it's obviously the main feed to that component. The helpful box illustrating C -1531 tells us that there are actually more than three connections, there are also take-off points for the radio and heated seat if fitted, and it gives us the position of the cables at the connector block.

That's actually all there is to the starting and charging circuits but, while we're on this diagram, let's have a look at a couple of other cables so you get a really clear idea of the way the diagram works.

Going back to the starter motor solenoid, there's another cable, number 50-1 coming from it which is SW-RT, or black with a red tracer. This actually disappears off our part of the diagram because it goes to a multi connector block C - 1939 which, a box tells us, is located in the engine compartment, but it comes back at the top right of our part and comes down to connector C -1151, a plug-in socket for the starter automatic transmission relay which is located in the fuse/relay box. You'll notice that there's also a black with blue tracer cable, number 50, going to this relay from the steering ignition switch. Another cable, number 31B-30, brown with white tracer, runs through another C connector to the automatic gear blocking switch. This is the sub-circuit that prevents the starter being energised on an automatic transmission car unless the gear selector is in P or N.

Also, from the steering ignition switch there's a black with yellow tracer cable number 15-4 which goes via a soldered join to connections C - 1108 and C - 1109 which, yet another box tells us, are fuses numbers 8 and 9. There don't seem to be any cables going from these fuses but remember that we are looking here at the main starting and charging diagram. If we looked at another part of the diagram we would see that fuses 8 and 9 are linked fuses in the fuse box feeding auxiliary circuits.

Similarly, from the alternator, a blue cable number 61 goes via a plain connector in the case of a petrol engine, or a connector with a diode in the case of a diesel, and again disappears off the part we're looking at. Tracing further on the full diagram shows that it goes to a connection C - 900 on the instrument panel and yet another helpful box tells us that cable 61 goes to the charge warning lamp. Also, a cable 61-2, blue with white tracer, goes to the automatic choke with connections shown for either a Solex or a Weber carburettor.

I could go over every sub-circuit on the whole diagram sorting it out for you but I'll leave that pleasure to you. It's a nice way of spending the evening when there's nothing very interesting on the 'box'.

Once you start breaking down the main diagram into its sub-circuits, all the mystery and headaches start to dissolve away - at least so far as tracing out the cables goes. When you're building a kit car and taking over a loom from a donor then, once you take the loom off, you won't have the handy location points for the C connections and the soldered joins which are given in the boxes on the diagram. It takes a little extra time to label each connector and soldered join when you're taking the loom off, but it makes sorting out what goes where on your kit car so much easier if you use small tie-on tags, like price labels, and number each connector as you disconnect the loom from the donor. Then, when you refer back to the donor's wiring diagram, you know what's what.

More confusing at first, but just as easy to sort out once you get down to it, is the 'cram it all in' type of wiring diagram. Ford was fond of using this on its earlier Capri models. Not only did they cram all the circuits on to one page, they also incorporated variations like manual or automatic transmission. The diagram was laid out with the components more or less in the position you find them on the car and, if you look at the example I've picked, you'll see that there are two batteries labelled 17 and 18, two starter solenoids 25 and 26, four starter motors 27, 28, 29 and 30, a dynamo 23 and an alternator 24. The two batteries and two solenoids are because the left-hand-drive auto transmission car had the battery on the opposite side from the manual transmission car, there were two types of starter offered, inertia or pre-engaged, for each transmission and the alternator was an RPO, or regular production option, in place of the dynamo. It all makes the diagram very crowded and very confusing even though things are helped by changes in wiring for auto transmission and alternator being shown as chain dotted.

The easiest thing to do with a diagram like this is to enlarge it on a photocopier - plenty of local stationery shops offer this for a modest sum - and then delete with Tippex or something similar all the cables that don't apply to your donor car. You end up with a diagram like the one for the Capri GT where the only RPOs shown chain dotted are for fog and driving lamps and dual horns. Once you get to this stage you can trace out the individual circuits as

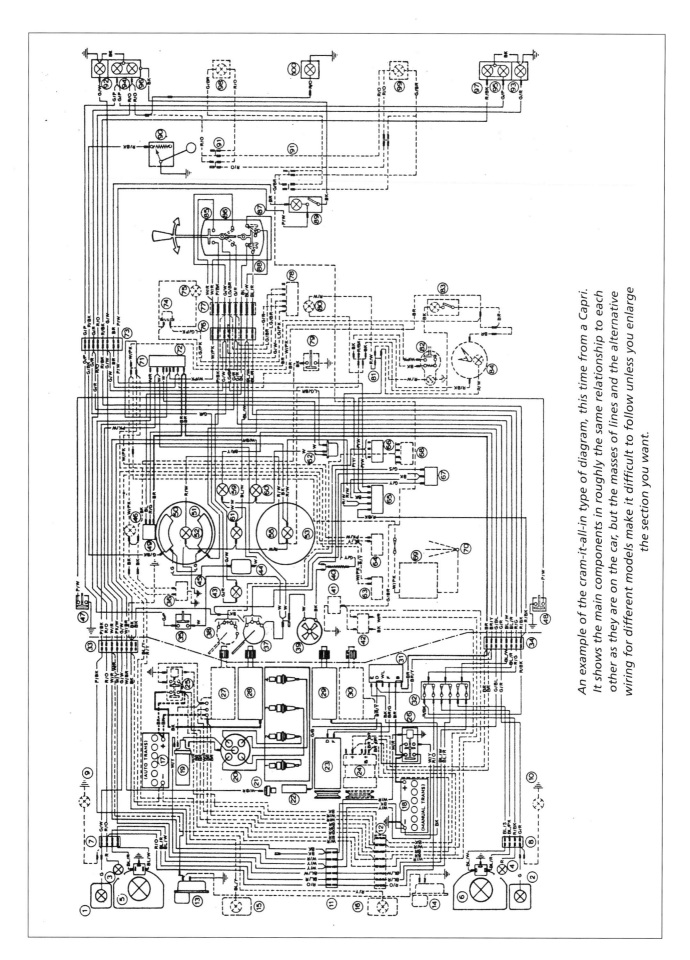

An example of the cram-it-all-in type of diagram, this time from a Capri. It shows the main components in roughly the same relationship to each other as they are on the car, but the masses of lines and the alternative wiring for different models make it difficult to follow unless you enlarge the section you want.

before. If it makes it easier, go over each one in a different coloured marker pen. You don't find any C connector points because they weren't used on the earlier Capris, but

One of the easiest diagrams for trouble shooting with a meter is the rail type with the positive rail at the top and the ground rail, or chassis earth, at the bottom. It's easy to follow what connects to what, but sometimes components shown near to each other are widely separated on the car.

the bulkhead connectors 33 and 34 and the front loom connectors 7, 8 and 11 are all labelled and help you to break the wiring down into its separate looms. The cables aren't numbered like the first example, but you can trace them from their colours.

Lastly, we get the rail type diagram so called because the battery is at one end of the diagram and there is a positive 'rail', usually along the top, and a negative or earth rail, usually along the bottom, though you may possibly find these transposed. It's a type of diagram used extensively in

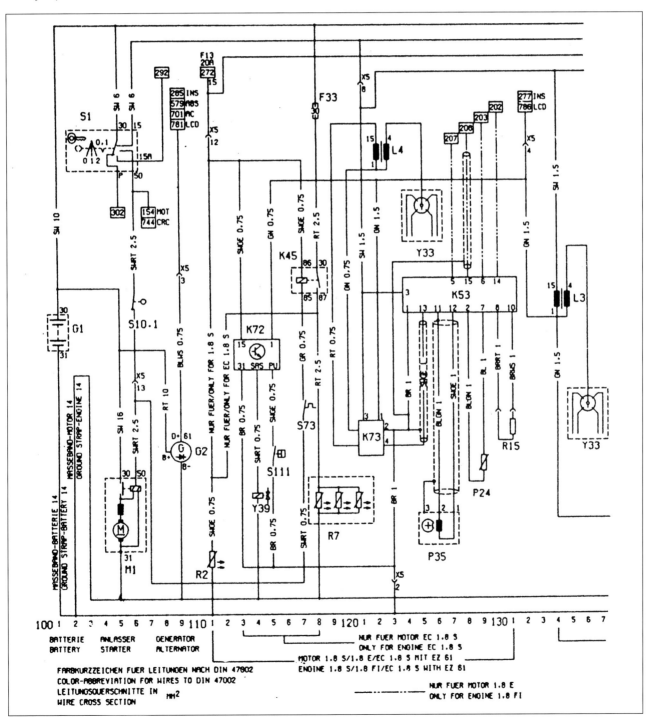

radio and television service sheets. The bottom rail is numbered so that you can locate components from a listed key. The diagram doesn't tell you where the cables run, but it gives you the cable colours so that you can identify them at each end of the loom. The components are identified by a letter and a number, usually with quite a logical code so that, for example, M stands for motor and S for switch, though G1 for the battery and G2 for the alternator are exceptions.

Sometimes, as here, the diagrams are intended for international use and there are notes under the bottom rail in several languages. Quite often, you find that a cable ends in a small square box with a number inside. The number refers you to the numbers along the bottom rail and means that the cable continues on another part of the diagram at this rail location where there will be another small box with a number referring back to the location of the first box. For example, at location 105 there is a cable coming from S1 (the starter switch) and ending in a box numbered 302. At location 302 on another part of the diagram there is a box numbered 105 which shows us that the cable goes to switch S5.4 which is a parking light switch.

You also find small abbreviations by some of the boxes.

Look at location 108 where, near the top of the diagram, there is a group of boxes with abbreviations INS, ABS, AC and LCD. The key to the diagram tells us that these stand for Instrument, Anti-lock Brake System, Air Conditioning and Liquid Crystal Display instrument. As well as the colour for the cable, there is a number which is the cross section of the cable is square millimetres, very helpful if you need to replace any of them as you know what size of cable to use. These abbreviations and cross section sizes all help to identify the cables more easily on the vehicle and on the diagram at the locations where they continue.

This type of diagram is purely theoretical and bears little if any relation to where the components are located on the car nor, and this can be confusing till you get used to it, to the distance apart of the components. Sometimes, a component that seems to be near to another one on the diagram is nowhere near it on the actual loom. These diagrams are very easy for trouble shooting with a meter but almost no help when you've got a loom off the donor and lying on the garage floor. The best thing to do if your donor has a diagram like this is to spend an hour or so before you take loom off the donor, sorting out, identifying and labelling the connections.

Chapter 5

MODIFYING STANDARD LOOMS

You can salvage a loom, buy a loom or, if you want to add extras, design your own modified looms. Here's how to set about it.

IN MOST CASES THE KIT MANUFACTURER WILL HAVE included instructions on how to modify a donor's loom or will offer a complete new loom for your car. Alternatively, you could go to one of the specialist loom making firms to have one made based on the old tatty donor loom. This may or may not give you all the cables you need if you want to add a load of electrical extras or if your donor loom is from a base model and you want to add the features of a GLS or whatever.

Another reason for modifying is that you might want to add features that didn't appear on any of the models of the donor car you use. For example, you might want to add intermittent wiper operation, plus heated washer jets to avoid freezing in winter, plus headlamp wash and wipe, plus intermittent rear window wipe plus rear window wash to a loom that catered only for two speed wipers with a single flick wipe. This would mean using a wiper motor and switch from a different model, maybe a more upmarket version of your donor or maybe a completely different car, plus the extra motors, relays and so on. It sounds like a complicated job, but it isn't all that difficult to modify a loom or make your own part loom which you

can combine with the main loom.

Before you can add to a loom, or modify it, you have to design the modifications. Well, you don't have to, but putting the extra circuits on paper makes things a lot easier and gives you a greater chance of success than trying to keep all the connections in mind while you're coping with masses of cables laid out on the garage floor or partly assembled into the car. Without a diagram you're bound to forget something. As well as the components, you'll need the wiring diagram for whatever the upmarket donor is to sort out the connections to the extra components.

By far the easiest way to design or add to a loom's circuits is to use the 'rail' type of diagram which I covered in the Chapter 4. The wiring diagram for your donor may not be a rail type but there's no reason why you shouldn't design your extra circuits as rails. Quite often, instead of a pair of rails, I draw a 'tree' diagram which is very similar except that the 'trunk' is the positive rail and the 'branches' are the sub-circuits. I also use the conventional 'line triangle' symbol for chassis earth instead of an earth rail because it means fewer lines on the paper so it's easier

Having an interior light is a useful feature you may be able to carry over from the donor car's loom. Alternatively, you might have to adapt the loom. Remember, this circuit will be Feed - Component - Switch - Earth.

Kits using older donor cars may well have a cooling fan driven off the engine. Converting to an electric fan will require some minor loom modification as well as perhaps making up dedicated mounting brackets for the fan itself.

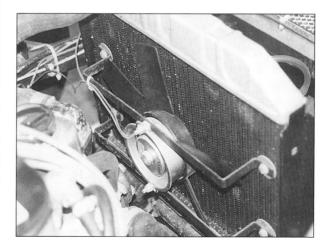

to draw and read. You'll find examples of tree diagrams in Chapter 6.

If I'm doing a job like this I find it gets less confusing if I delete from the old loom any cables which fed components I'm not going to use and add all the new cables I want to feed the new components. You can, if you like, use some of the existing cables in your loom that feed the wiper motor or whatever, but from experience I find this can get confusing. What you must be careful of is that you don't delete any loop-feed cables or loop-earth cables. You sometimes find this on multi-purpose switches where the feed to the switch is the feed for more than one component. You can check this from the wiring diagram and, as a double check, follow carefully the feeds backwards from the fuse if the fuse to the component you're deleting also protects something else.

Talking of fuses, this is a good place to bring in the extra fuses you'll need if you're adding extra electrics. In the conversion I'm talking about here you'll need several, and some donor cars are woefully short in this respect. The old Escorts, for example, had quite basic electrics with only seven fuses - only six fuses on pre-1969 cars. You've got a choice here. Either you can add extra in-line fuses or you can change the fuse board for one from an more upmarket car. I'm a great believer in having lots of fuses like separate fuses for each main headlamp beam, each dipped headlamp beam, left-hand side and tail lights, right hand side and tail lights and so on. I hate to be left completely in the dark if a fuse blows, having experienced this one dark night on a winding country road and narrowly avoiding a spot of hedging and ditching at high speed.

I also hate unnecessary unfused circuits where a short can lead to fire. There are enough necessary unfused circuits in a car without adding to them. Use line fuses if you like, I've got nothing against them, but the more fuses you have on the main board the less hassle it is to change a fuse if one blows. With lots of line fuses you have to grope and ferret, which isn't the best of ideas on a dark

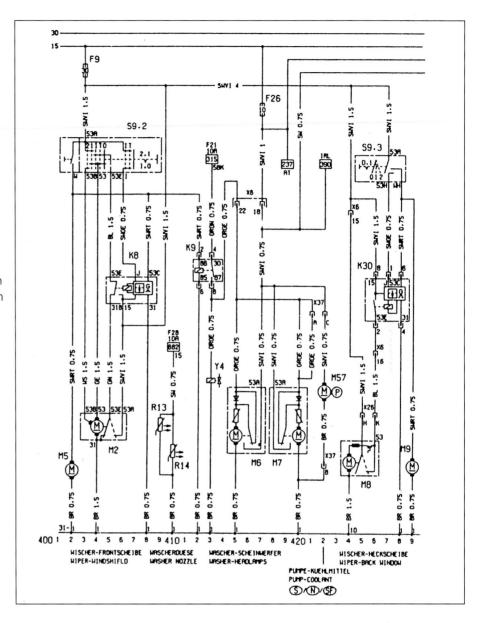

The wiring diagram for the up-market wash-wipe and associated systems on a Vauxhall Carlton. These circuits could easily be incorporated in a kit car loom.

wet night.

A very handy fuse board for adding lots of electrics, or extra fusing if you haven't got many fuses, is the one from a Vauxhall Carlton from 1986 onwards. The fuse board is nice and easy to lift out, complete with its mounting, so it shouldn't be too difficult to find somewhere to mount it in a kit car. It's got mountings for several relays and, best of all, it's got provision for up to 30 fuses. Even with 30 fuses you won't be able to fuse every single component separately, but you can choose your grouping so that, if a fuse blows, you don't get more than one important component going dead at a time.

Another nice thing about the Carlton fuse board, though

Above: A good example of a well-stocked fuse board which is easy to move from a donor car to a kit car. This one, unfortunately, has a burnt patch where someone had stupidly wired across a fuse which kept blowing, instead of tracing the fault first. Below: Another useful auxiliary fuse board which I spotted in a breaker's yard.

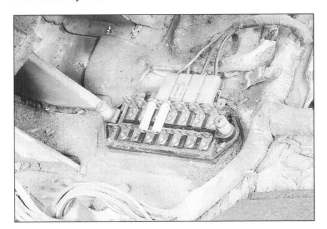

it's not unique in this respect, is that, if the fuse contacts get damaged or corroded you can replace them individually just by pushing the new ones into the slots in the plastic. At the time of writing, fuse connectors to fit to the board cost 15p each from Vauxhall dealers.

The Carlton board isn't by a long chalk the only one you can use so it pays to have a good look round a breaker's yard that deals with modern insurance write-off cars and pick a comprehensive one that's going to be easiest to fit in your car and give you all the fuses you want. Even if the board has got a section for relays they won't all be on it, so while you're about it get the relay mounting boards as well. Some Japanese cars have lovely relay mounting boards under the bonnet, often on an inner wing where they're easy to get at. You can pick up lots of ideas, hints and tips about wiring up electrics just by wandering round a breakers with your eyes open and your mind in gear.

When you come to wire up a new, larger, fuse board it's best to follow, as far as you can, the feeds to the fuse board the same as the donor from which it came. If you look at a rail wiring diagram you'll see that there are only two main feeds for all the circuits, one direct from the battery (or from the starter solenoid terminal which goes direct to the battery), and one from the ignition switch. It varies slightly from car to car which components get direct feed and which come live only when the ignition is switched on. Obviously, you want things like lights, courtesy lights, hazard flashers, central locking system and so on to work when the ignition is off, plus anything you might want to use when the ignition key's not turned on, like a map reading light, under-bonnet light, boot light and radio or stereo system.

On many cars you switch the ignition key to position 1 to get a live feed to all the other circuits, including the radio, but my preference is to be able to switch on the radio without having to use the ignition key. The coil, fuel pump and, if fitted, fuel injection system, are added when the key is at position 2. Position 3, which is spring loaded, brings in the starter. The reason for having the coil and fuel system on position 2, the normal running position, is that you can have any of the other ignition-controlled auxiliaries live without heating up the coil and injection components and having the fuel pump under pressure when the engine isn't running. On a

Left: Bind your new cables into the main loom after you've checked everything.

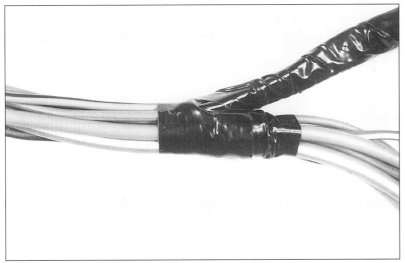

few cars you'll find that only the radio comes live at position 1 but I prefer to have some other ignition-controlled circuits live as well so that you can work on them, test them and, if necessary, trouble-shoot them without having the coil and fuel system live. Things vary from maker to maker so, if you're putting in a new fuse board, you can more or less please yourself.

Sometimes when you use a large fuse board you'll find that some of the fuses for the ignition controlled circuits are linked so that you only have to take one feed cable from the ignition switch and the lot come live. The same sometimes applies when you have the left and right headlamps and side and tail lamps fused separately, one cable from the lighting switch feeds the fuses for all the lights. This is common but, being a niggling old fusspot, I prefer to have separate feed cables from the switch to the lights on the right and left of the car. Once again, it's this phobia I've got about being left completely in the dark at speed on a winding country road, but you please yourself. In some cases, you might have to do some looping at the back of the fuse board to get what you want. On the whole, though, it's easiest to follow the same system as the donor from which the fuse board came.

Talking of fuses leads us to what rating of fuses you need to fit. There's a very simple law about electrics which says that the power in watts equals the current in amps multiplied by the voltage. If we transpose this equation we see that amps equals watts divided by volts. So, if you've got a lamp, for example, rated at 60 watts, and the voltage is 12, the current will be 60 divided by 12 which equals 5 amps.

That doesn't mean that you would fit a 5 amp fuse because you've got to allow a margin. First, you've got to allow for surge current. When you switch a circuit on it takes a fraction of a second or so for things to settle down during which you get a surge of current. Think of it as giving the circuit a kick to wake it up. This surge can be around 150 per cent of the steady running current so when they're first switched the lamps could take a surge current of 7.5 amps. Allow a safety margin because you don't want to keep blowing fuses, and call it 10 amps. Then, the ordinary type of car fuses you buy aren't close tolerance components like you get in electronics. They're quite cheap and cheerful things and could be anything between plus and minus 20 per cent of the figure marked on them. Allow for this, and call the fuse rating 15 amps. This means that the fuse could blow at anything between about 12 amps and 18 amps.

In normal use a 60 watt lamp won't take 12 amps, even on surge, so it won't keep blowing the fuse. If there were a dead short, the current would shoot up way beyond 18

amps before things had time to heat up enough to cause a fire, so the fuse would blow and the car would be protected. It all sounds a bit crude, a bit like take away the number you first thought of but, as a general rule for car fusing, work out the nominal steady current the component will use and multiply this by three to get the nominal fuse rating. The nearest usual fuse rating to 15 amps is 16 amps so that's the one we'd fit.

More or less in the same area as fuses are relays. People often get puzzled by relays because they're little sealed black boxes and you can't see what goes on inside them. Actually, they're quite simple. Inside the box you've got an electrical switch which is switched on by quite a low amperage current, typically 3 to 4 amps. The switch itself, however, can carry a much higher current, 30 or 50 amps if necessary, depending on the design and rating of the relay.

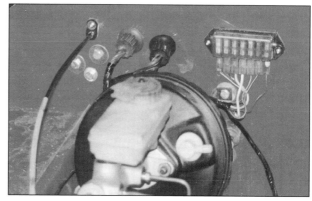

Above: This Cortina based Eagle RV has simple electrics which make it easy to retain the donor's loom. Here you can see the Cortina's fuse box as well as its neat bulkhead plugs which take the engine loom through into the cabin. Below: If you do not have these plugs, you'll have to be careful to use large rubber grommets to protect the loom from damage as it goes through the bulkhead/panel.

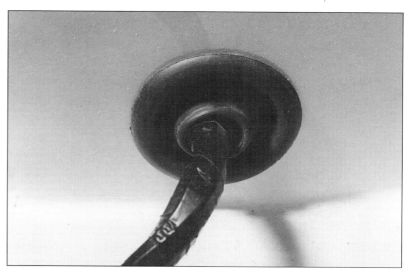

Using relays has two big advantages over using a simple switched circuit. It means that you can reduce the current at dashboard or steering column switches, which reduces the arcing across the contacts when they open or close, and you can use much lighter wiring up to the switches which makes it easier to group the cables in a loom.

Relays vary in design and the number of terminals or plug-in contacts but, if you look at them in a circuit diagram you'll see that they have a switching circuit and an operating circuit, or sometimes more than one operating circuit. Sometimes you may find that there is a fuse incorporated in the relay box, the relay for the Cortina heated rear window, which has a 16 amp fuse, being one example.

OK, I've covered the preliminaries, now let's look at a circuit in detail, the one I mentioned earlier about upgrading the wipe and wash circuits. I mentioned the Carlton fuse box just now, and a Carlton is a very good example of upmarket wash-wipe. I'll run through the circuits on the wiring diagram, which is rail type and nice and easy to follow (see page 34).

Line 15 at the top is the feed for circuits controlled by the ignition. In other words, line 15 is live when the ignition is switched on. Line 31 at the bottom is chassis earth. Fuses are labelled F, switches are labelled S, relays are labelled K, motors are labelled M.

S9.2, at location 400-409, is the main wiper switch with intermittent control and S9.3, at 425-428, is the rear window wiper switch with intermittent control. K8, at 404-408, is the windscreen wiper intermittent relay, K9, at 411-414, is the headlamp washer relay and K30, at 426-428, is rear window wiper intermittent relay. M5, at 402, is the screen washer pump, M2, at 404, is the wiper motor, M6 and M7, at 416 and 420, are the headlamp wiper motors, M8, at 424, is the rear window wiper motor and M9, at 429, is the rear window washer pump. R13 and R14, at 410, are the heated washer jets and Y4, at 413, is the headlamp washer solenoid valve. You'll need all these bits if you're going to use the complete system. The points marked X are plug-in connectors on the Carlton's loom.

It's vital, when you're getting a system like this from a donor which is different from your main donor, to take the short looms and connectors as well as the components, or, if you can't for any reason get the short loom, at least take a good length of cabling with each component and the connector to it. Make sure also that you get suitable sockets for the relays to plug in. Leave some of the bits out and you're going to be stuck when you come to wire the components into your car.

There are a few lines on the diagram which aren't relevant to this part of the circuit. For example, the

Below: Multi-pin connectors like these are very useful for adding circuits. Look for them on up-market cars in breakers. Right: If the pins are corroded you remove them by pushing down a small tag inside the connector. Lucas sells new pins ready to solder to the cable.

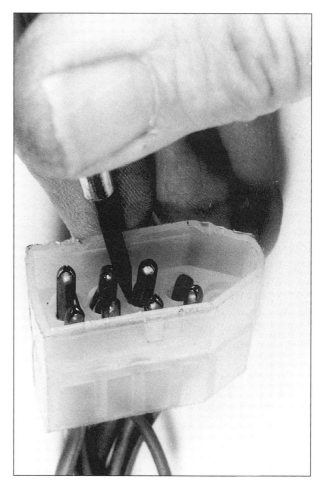

horizontal rail just below F9, at 403, runs off the diagram to feed things like the horns. Some of the little square boxes with numbers in them refer to other parts of the wiring diagram which deal mainly with options on the Carlton like electric sunroofs, ABS, air conditioning, cruise control and so on and don't affect the bits I'm dealing with.

A 10-amp fuse F26, at 417, protects M6 and M7, and a 30-amp fuse F9, at 403, protects M5, M2, M8 and M9 via their respective relays and switches. R13 and R14 are protected by fuse F28 which is not on this part of the diagram but is at location 272, together with the wash/wipe switch, as the box at location 410 shows. Similarly, relay K9 plus M6 and M7 are protected by fuse F21 at location 315, as the box at 413 indicates.

When you come to connect the cables for your new, extra, components, put your main donor loom, or the loom from the kit maker, in place and held by temporary ties before you start on the extras. Then wire in each extra complete before you go on to another one, using more temporary ties to hold the cables to your main loom.

On a rail diagram, which is purely theoretical and doesn't represent any sort of layout on the car, you often find T-junctions in the cables. As a case in point, look at K9, the relay for the headlamp washers. From terminal 87 on the relay you've got a cable which goes to Y4, the solenoid valve with a T-junction going to connector X6 and, just below that, another T-junction to take cables to M6 and M7, the headlamp wiper motors. This doesn't mean you've got to make T-junctions in the cables, though you may have to sometimes and I'll deal with how to make them later. In this case, I would use a double connector at terminal 87 of the relay and either a double connector at X6 or go directly from X6 to one motor and use a double connector to take a second feed to the other motor. Unless you follow the system on the donor car, which is always the best plan if it's convenient, you can please yourself how you wire depending on how convenient it is to run the cables in your particular car.

When you've got all your components in place and connected, put in the relevant fuses and test each circuit before you go any further. Only when you're completely happy with all the additions you've made to the basic loom do you go along with tape and bind in the extra cables to make things neat and tidy. I'll deal with binding up a loom in a later chapter.

Above: The use of a 'chocolate block' connector may seem like the answer to your wiring prayers, but it is not. Don't use them as they are not designed for areas that may get damp or wet and will not provide a clean contact. Below: Some steering column switches, like this one, have studs underneath to take the cables. Others have flat push-on connectors.

If you can't find room on the fuse board you can use in-line fuses for some components like the radio.

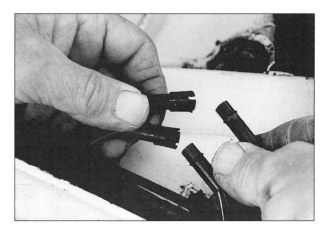

38

Of course, if you do something like I've outlined here, you won't be able to use the steering column switches from your original donor car because they won't have the necessary contacts on them. Here, I'm afraid you're rather on your own because it would be impossible for me to go through all the steering columns you're likely to use and all the switches you're likely to use. However, on most modern cars that you're likely to use as donors for extra electrics, the multi-purpose stalk switches on the steering column clip into place on plastic housings which attach to the outer part of the column. Sometimes you have to do quite a lot of modification but it shouldn't be beyond the wit of a good kit car builder to devise some way to adapt things even if it means making up extra bracket plates and adapting the plastic steering column shroud pieces.

You'll also have to work out which cables for the components you haven't added, like headlamp dip, headlamp main beam, headlamp flash and so on, go to which terminals on your new switches. Unless you expect your kit car to go together like an Airfix model kit it's the sort of thing you have to expect, and solving these little problems is part of the challenge, and satisfaction, of building a kit car which is individual to you.

If you fit a new multi-purpose steering column stalk switch for the wipers you'll naturally want to fit the matching one for the indicators, and you might be puzzled by part of the wiring to this on some modern cars. When the ignition is switched on, the indicator switch, quite naturally, operates the indicators. However, when the ignition is off (VWs being a case in point), the indicator switch sometimes feeds the side and tail parking lights on the side to which you turn the switch or, sometimes, only on one side. The idea is that you can use the parking lights on one side only as a safety feature when you park in an unlit road, or on the wrong side of the road, without having the drain of four lights on your battery. On the other hand, if you forget to centralise the indicator switch when you leave the car for a couple of days you can come back to find the battery completely dead. It's a little bit of electrickery which you don't have to use, but you can spend a few happy minutes working out the circuit from the wiring diagram if the upmarket donor you use has this feature.

Oh yes, remember to keep a copy, plus a spare copy just in case, of all the modifications you make to the electrics otherwise you're going to be right up the creek without a paddle if, some time in the future, something stops working and you haven't got a wiring diagram to start fault finding.

Chapter 6

DESIGNING A CIRCUIT FROM SCRATCH

If your donor car loom's a bit tatty and you don't want to
fork out for a professionally made loom, then you could always design
your own. Here's how.

PROBABLY NINE KIT CAR BUILDERS OUT OF TEN WILL USE either a donor's loom or a modified donor loom or, possibly, a new loom supplied by the kit manufacturer. However, if you're the tenth and want to design your own circuits and make up your own loom, here's how to set about it. I can't cover every single electrical component you might want to fit and I'm certainly not going to attempt to design from scratch the circuits for an electronic engine management system. But I've designed basic car circuits from scratch and you can, too, if you take care.

Drawing up a wiring diagram for your kit car, and then wiring from it, isn't nearly as difficult as most people imagine. The problems all begin to fall away once you start thinking of groups of circuits instead of trying to take in the whole shooting match at once.

There are three main sections in a car's electrics. The first is the starting, charging and ignition, the second is the lighting, and the third is the group of accessories controlled through the ignition switch such as instruments, wipers and so on. You can think of each of these as a tree with branches coming from it. I've separated the hazard flasher circuit from these because it usually has two feeds, one from the lighting tree and one from the ignition controlled tree.

Colour coding is essential if you want to avoid getting into a terrible muddle, and, as I said earlier, there's a British Standard which lays down the recommended colours for each circuit. Most British-made cars used to use the BS colours, though a lot of them don't any more because, with multi-national car makers, many of them aren't designed in Britain. Ford is another case altogether. Ford always went its own sweet way with colour coding, and often varied it from model to model so, if you're basing the electrics on parts from various donors I'd advise forgetting about the colour coding given in the manual except as a guide to the charging system, and possibly for identifying the grouped cables to things like the instrument panel and the control stalk on the steering column.

These last two often have multi-plug connectors to plug into the main loom, and if the cables to these are in good order, you can leave the cables attached to the stalk and panel and rewire just the main looms from scratch. It's an individual choice, but don't worry if you need to renew the whole of the wiring. Multi-plugs were brought in as a production convenience, though they also help in servicing. If you want to you can buy new multi-plugs and put them in. Whatever you do, try to keep some order into your choice of colours, and don't mix similar colours in dissimilar circuits. That's an easy way to problems.

There are ten main colours used in the British Standards code, and these are subdivided again by using tracers, a thin line of colour different from the main colour of the cable. Altogether, there are 133 separate combinations listed by British Standards, each one for a different part of a circuit group, and you won't want to buy dozens of lengths of cable, each with a different main colour and tracer. Even so, it's worthwhile sticking to the code for the ten main colours, and then using short push-on coloured sleeves to identify individual cables in the loom. So, for example, if the Standard calls for a blue cable with a red tracer, you could use plain blue with red sleeves on the ends.

The 10 main colours are:

Black: all earth leads.
Blue: headlamps.
Brown: battery main feeds not ignition controlled.
Green: fused accessories controlled by the ignition switch.
Purple: fused accessories not controlled by the ignition switch.
Orange: wiper circuits, fused, controlled by the ignition switch.
White: unfused accessories controlled by the ignition switch
Slate (or grey): window lifts.
Yellow: odds and ends such as overdrive circuit, door locks, fuel injection, automatic gearbox inhibitor and so on.

Do watch out for that black colour. Even though the British Standard uses it for earth leads, many makers use it for live leads after the switch, so be warned.

When you're looking at circuits, and planning them, it's important to keep two golden rules in mind. I know I've mentioned them before, but I'm mentioning them again because they're important. There are only two basic ways a circuit can be wired. These are: **feed - switch - component - earth**; and **feed - component - switch - earth**. Sidelights are an example of the first way, and door courtesy lights are an example of the second. Keep this in mind when you're drawing your diagrams, and when you're trouble shooting. Remember, for example, that the cables to and from the interior light are live even though the light is off.

We talked earlier about groups of circuits. Let's have a look at the starting, charging and ignition group. If you

The basic starting, charging and ignition circuit using a Lucas ACR alternator and non-electronic ignition.

look at the diagram below, the main heavy feed cable from the battery to the starter motor is easy enough to identify, and isn't colour coded. Then from the solenoid you get one cable which feeds all the other circuits, and goes via the ammeter, if there's one fitted, though because of the high current demands of modern electrics we don't recommend an ammeter. A battery condition indicator, which is a voltmeter, is much easier to fit and much safer from a fire hazard point of view.

We said all the other circuits, but there are exceptions which we'll come to later. From the solenoid, one cable goes to the ignition switch and another goes off to the lights tree. The first position on the ignition switch usually

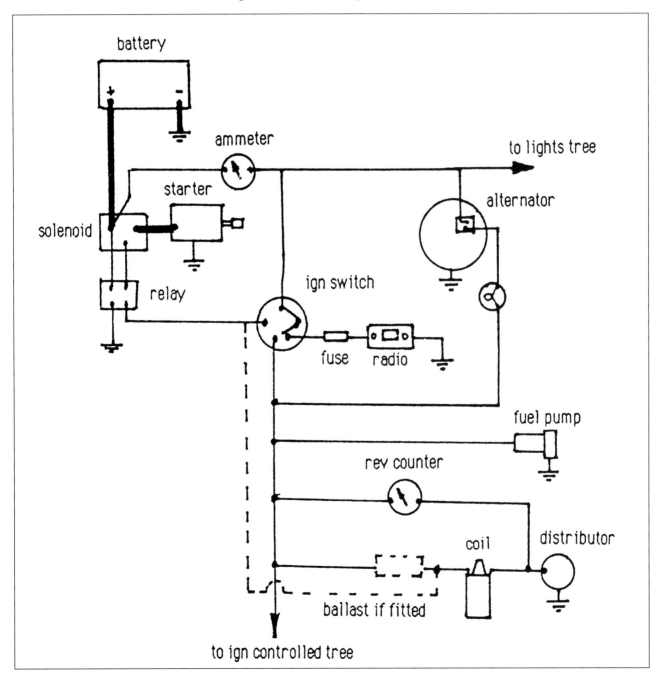

brings in just the radio circuit so you can listen to this with the engine stopped and without heating up the coil. The second position, normal running, brings in the circuits live so that the charge warning light comes on, the electric fuel pump is live and the coil is live. If you've got an electronic rev counter fitted, this will also be live. Also live will be the feed to the circuits controlled by the ignition switch, the instruments, wipers, heater blower and so on. The third position of the switch, the spring-loaded 'engine start' position, energises the starter relay to start the engine.

There are again exceptions, but the wiring diagram for the donor from which you got the switch will tell which is which.

Some cars, including many Fords, have a coil which normally works on 9 volts, with a ballast resistor in the feed. For starting, the ballast resistor is by-passed by a feed from the 'engine start' position of the ignition switch, so theoretically the coil is over-run at 12 volts to give a good spark. In practice, as I noted earlier, the battery is seldom quite fully charged, and there is such a drain from the starter motor that the actual voltage to the coil when the ballast resistor is by-passed is nearer 9.5 to 10 volts.

A third cable goes to the charging circuit. I've drawn a wiring circuit for a current Lucas ACR alternator with the European Terminations System. If you've got a Lucas A-series alternator, or a Bosch alternator, the connections are very similar but, once again, refer to the donor circuit wiring diagram.

The Lucas ACR charging circuit is simplicity itself. There are three terminals at the connecting block on the alternator, but two are linked so in effect there are only two. The linked pair are the ones which take the cable from the solenoid, and on high output alternators the cable is duplicated to avoid having an inconveniently heavy cable to carry the heavy current. The other terminal goes to the charge warning light, and the body of the alternator is earthed through the engine.

I mentioned two more feeds coming off the starting and charging circuit, one from the battery side of the solenoid, or from the battery itself, so it's live all the time, and one live only when the ignition is switched on. These two feed all the other circuits, and for these we think in 'trees', a main trunk, with sub-trunks or sub-trees, and lots of branches. Quite often, a component is fed through a relay. This is just an electric switch with heavy-duty contacts inside to take a heavy current. These contacts are operated by a control feed which takes only a small current so you can use a light-duty switch.

The sub-tree which is live all the time is for the lights, and though to simplify the diagram I've drawn the lighting switch, the dip switch and headlamp flasher separately, they're often combined in one steering column stalk. The lighting circuits, except the interior light, are all feed - switch - component - earth type. I've drawn the headlamp and the side and rear lamp circuits as split into left hand and right hand, each with its own fuse. This is the modern recommended way, and has the advantage that should a fuse blow you aren't left completely in the dark.

Current lighting regulations allow you to have fog lights, front and rear, on when the sidelights are on, but long-range driving lights and spot lights may be on only when the headlamps are on main beam, so these are wired in the main beam tree. There is a link feed to the headlamp flash switch so that it can flash the main beams whatever the position of the main lighting switch or the dip switch. I've drawn the link without a fuse, which is normal practice, but you can put one in if you feel safer with it.

I've put boot light, glove box light and map light in the sidelights tree so that they can be used only when the sidelights are on. If you want them to come on when the sidelights are off, put them in the same tree as the interior light. On some cars the boot and glove box lights have pin switches, the sort used in doors for interior courtesy lights, so the light comes on when the glove box lid or boot door is opened. In this case they're the feed - component - switch - earth type of circuit, the same as the interior light.

You'll notice that the horn circuit has two fuses. First there is the branch fuse, which fuses the control part of the horn relay, then there's a separate fuse for the heavier current to the horn itself. A very similar circuit is used if you want an electric radiator fan. On some donor cars you may find the radiator fan branch on the ignition-controlled tree, but I prefer to have it wired so that it continues to operate after you switch the engine off. This helps to avoid local overheating as the engine cools down. The circuit is exactly the same as the horn, except that the thermostatic switch takes the place of the horn push.

The flashing indicators circuit needs a little explanation. You'll see that there are two feeds to the hazard switch, one from the lighting tree, and a second from the tree for accessories controlled by the ignition. Each feed has its own fuse. When the hazard switch is off, the flashers are fed from the ignition-controlled circuit and are controlled by the normal steering column stalk. When the hazard switch is on, the feed changes to the lighting tree, so you don't have to have the ignition on.

Moving on to the ignition-controlled tree (see page 44), the top branch is for an automatic choke. If you fit a manual choke, just delete the choke solenoid, and the automatic thermostat switch becomes the manual switch, or cable, on the choke control. The second branch has a sub-tree, and feeds the instruments, heater, screen washer and some of the warning lights. Depending on the type of instruments you use, you might or might not have a voltage stabiliser in the instrument feed. I've drawn one in the feed to the fuel gauge and engine temperature gauge. If your instruments don't need a voltage stabiliser, just leave it out and draw the feeds back to the sub-tree. If more instruments need a stabiliser, feed them from the output side of the stabiliser. Once again, check the diagram for the donor car.

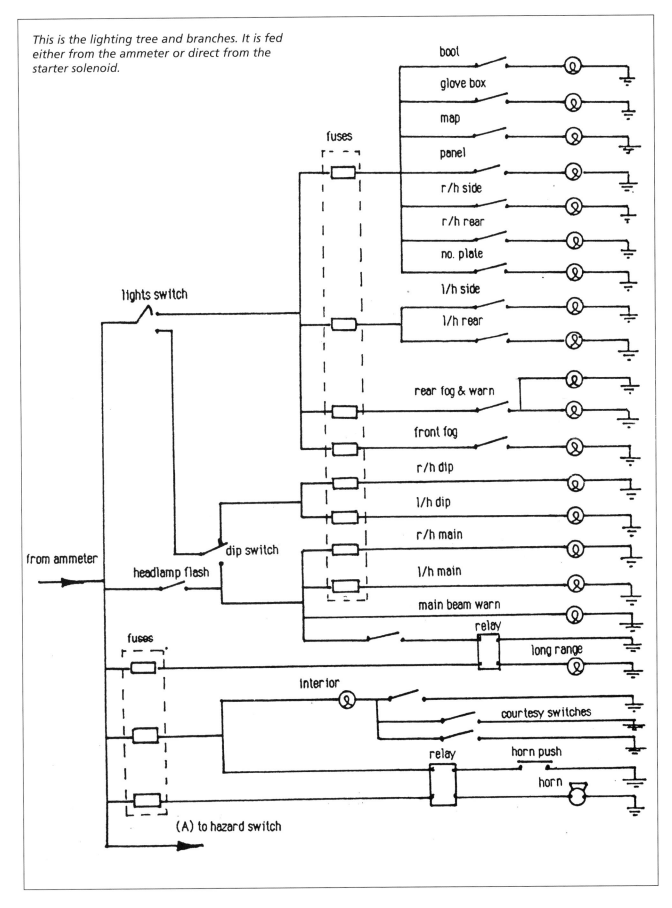

This is the lighting tree and branches. It is fed either from the ammeter or direct from the starter solenoid.

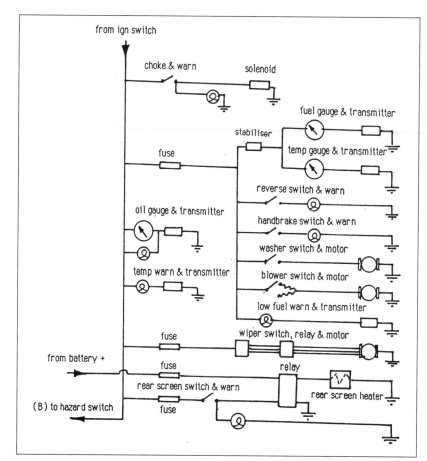

The tree for the ignition controlled accessories and instruments which are live only when the ignition is switched on.

diagram of the donor car might show it using the same warning light as the handbrake. This is usual, and both circuits are the feed - component - switch - earth type. If you want to use separate warning lights, draw the low brake fluid warning branch separately as a feed - component - switch - earth type.

The wiper motor branch I've drawn here is purely diagrammatic. There are so many different types of wiper - single speed, two-speed, with or without delay or flick-wipe, linked to the screen wash or not - that there just isn't room to draw them all. This is one branch you will have to sort out from the wiring diagram for the donor car. I've drawn the washer separate from the wiper switch.

At the bottom of the tree, we get to the control branch for the rear screen heater. Screen heaters take a lot of current, and have to be switched via a relay. Like the horn, the control feed to the screen heater relay has its own fuse, and there is a separate fuse in the heavy main feed to the relay. Because a screen heater takes so much current it isn't usual for this main feed to be on one of the trees, nor is it usual for it to be through the ammeter. The usual method is to take the feed straight from battery positive, either at the starter solenoid or at a junction box.

I've covered all the main circuits, but there are several more things you want to fit such as rear screen wash/wipe and bulb failure monitor. If your donor car hasn't got them, get

The hazard flasher circuit has two feeds, one from the lights tree and one from the ignition controlled tree.

Right at the bottom of this sub-tree is the warning light for low fuel level. I've drawn the transmitter for this as a separate unit, but in some cases it's combined with the fuel level indicator in the tank, with its own terminal.

Because oil pressure is so vital to the engine, it's usual for an electric oil pressure gauge and warning light to be wired on a branch of their own without a fuse, though you can, of course, put fuses in every branch and sub branch if you want to. I've drawn the warning light and pressure gauge transmitters as combined, though on some cars they are separate. Again, check with the wiring diagram of your donor car. I also like to have the engine temperature warning light wired on its own without a fuse.

Some cars have the stop lamp feed wired into the ignition-controlled tree, and some have it off the main lighting trunk with its own fuse so that the feed to the stop lamp switch is live all the time. I've left it off, so you can put it wherever you please.

I've drawn the handbrake warning light as a feed - switch - component - earth circuit, but some handbrakes are wired as a feed - component - switch - earth circuit. If you've got a brake fluid reservoir with a low brake fluid warning switch in the lid, the wiring

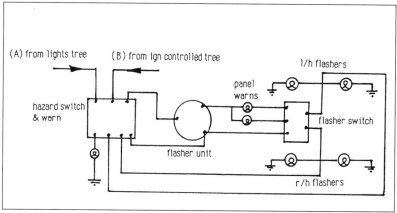

the necessary components from a car in a breakers (the Rover SD1 is a good source for a bulb monitor). Trace the circuits for these from the wiring diagram for the car you get them from.

By now you should be able to list all the electrical equipment you want in your car, and draw out the trees and branches for a wiring diagram. I haven't got room to cover every possible electrical component on a car, but if you want to add something else, such as an under-bonnet light, mobile phone charger or whatever, decide whether you want them controlled by the ignition switch, or the lighting switch, or available when everything else is off, and draw another branch in the appropriate place. Always keep in mind the feed - switch - component - earth or feed - component - switch - earth rules, and you shouldn't have any problems. Now let's look at how to convert these diagrams into practical wiring on the car.

FROM SCHEMING TO PRACTICE

So far I've been looking at schematic diagrams. Before you can start wiring, you have to convert these to practical

From the schematics you construct a practical wiring diagram. This one is for the auxiliaries controlled by the ignition switch. The abbreviations trans *on the cables from the three gauges stands for transmitter, or sensor.*

diagrams. When you're actually doing the work it makes things easier if you split the electrics up into separate circuits, just as I did with the schematics, so get yourself a few large pieces of paper and sketch out a plan of your car with the electrical components in the same positions they'll be on the car.

On the schematics I used a trunk feed with branches coming from it, and though I suppose it's possible to wire a car like this, it isn't the easiest way, and you'd need a lot of junction boxes. In practice I use either loop wiring or in-line splitters and, occasionally, soldered joins. How you route the cables depends on the layout of your car, but try to avoid having more than two wires going to any one terminal on a component. It's best with a plug-in type of component to have just one wire at the plug-in terminal and, if necessary, to make soldered T-junctions.

Let's look at an example. Take the schematic diagram of the auxiliaries controlled by the ignition switch, and suppose we have a manual, not automatic, choke with a warning light on the choke switch. I would probably run a feed from the ignition switch to the choke switch, and from there to one of the three fuses on that trunk. Then loop to the other two fuses, then to the oil pressure gauge, then to the warning lights and from there to the hazard switch. If I wanted a fuse in the hazard circuit then I would use a fourth fuse in the fuse box if there was one spare. If not, I

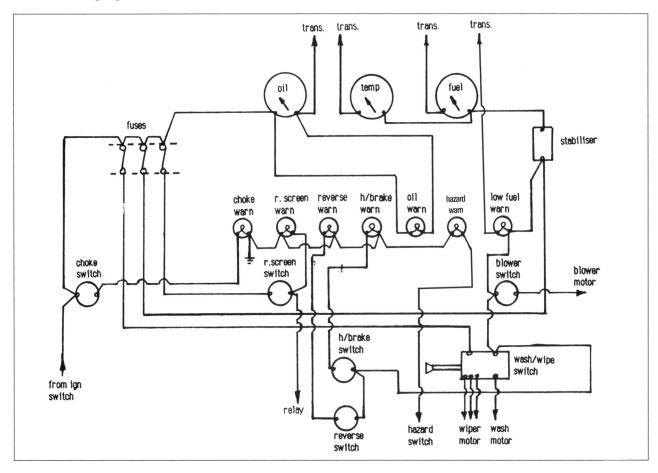

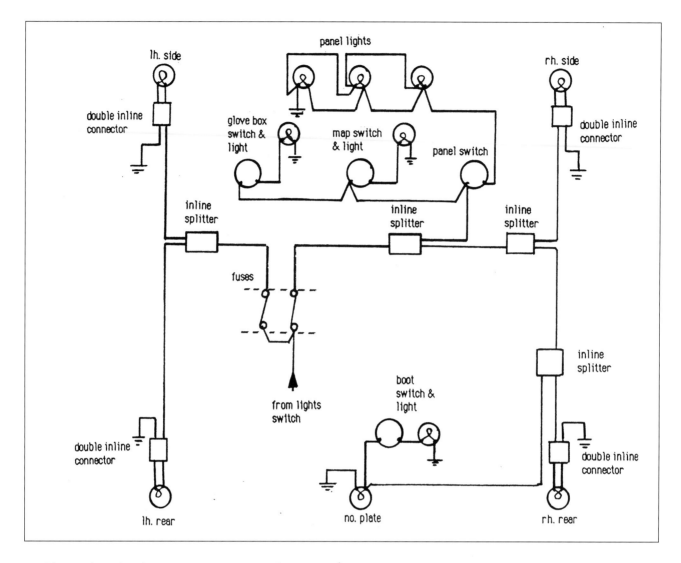

would use either a line fuse or a separate auxiliary fuse board which would give me extra fuses for other circuits and keep them all together where they would be easier to find than several separate line fuses.

From the fused side of the fuse box, separate feeds would run to the rear screen heater switch and the wiper switch, but with the other components I start looping again. Depending on the layout of the components, the feed could go to the stabiliser and from there to the low fuel warning light, because these would be likely to be near each other. Then I might carry on to the blower switch, and then to the washer switch. Depending on the type of washer switch, it might be easy to couple two feed wires to its terminal, and then run to the handbrake switch on the transmission tunnel and from there to the reverse light switch on the gearbox. If it wasn't easy to couple two wires on a stalk-type washer switch, or if it was awkward to take an extra cable to a steering column stalk switch, I would either use a soldered T-join or put an in-line splitter in the feed after leaving the blower switch. One of the split feeds would go to the washer switch and the other to the

This is the practical layout guide derived from the schematic for the sidelamp circuits. I've used in-line splitters to avoid running too many long cables from front to back, though you can use soldered T-junctions. I've also used double in-line connectors to make it easy to take off the sidelamp and headlamp units.

handbrake switch. Look how I've arranged it in the practical wiring diagram, and then do something similar for your car.

Similarly, look on the lighting circuit schematic above, at the branch feeding the right-hand sidelight, right-hand rear light, number plate, panel lights, map light, glove box light and boot light.

Here, I would either run two cables from the fused side of the fuse box, or use a splitter after coming from the fuse box, whichever was more convenient. If I used two cables at the fuse box, then to save running a cable to the right-hand sidelight and back again to loop to the right-hand rear light, one of the two feeds from the fuse box or from the splitter would have another in-line splitter, and the two feeds from this would go to the right-hand sidelight and the right-hand rear light. From the rear light I would use a loop to the number plate light and then on to the boot light.

The other feed from the fuse box would go to the panel light switch, and from there loop to the map light and glove box light. You'll probably have more than one panel lamp, and it's often awkward to loop a cable to the bulb holder. In that case, use a small junction box, and mount it somewhere behind the dash.

When you've drawn your component layout diagrams you might have to make one or two tries lightly in pencil before you get the most convenient cable runs, but you'll soon get the hang of it. If you're using a ready-wired or printed circuit instrument panel from the donor car, use the wiring diagram in the donor car's workshop manual to see where the feeds go.

You could leave your practical wiring diagram as it is, but it's got one drawback. You would have to undo individual connections to take a component off the car. To avoid this, use in-line connectors to things you might want to take off. Good examples are the lights. Most headlights, either sealed beam or the block lens type with bulbs, connect with spade terminals having three blades, one for the main beam, one for the dipped beam and one for earth. You have a single connector to fit these, with three wires coming from it.

This would defeat your looping principle, and also mean that if you wanted to take off a front panel or a wing with more than one lamp on it you would have to unsolder a number of cables. To avoid this, use in-line connectors so that you can, for example, take off a wing complete with its headlight, sidelight and flasher light by just unplugging three connectors instead of groping about undoing separate cables. Use these in-line connectors anywhere where you think it might be convenient.

Another good place is in the group of cables that go to steering column stalk switches. If you need to take the

switch off, or take the steering column out, you only have to unplug. You'll probably find that the steering column switches from the donor car have cables which finish in a multi-pin in-line connector, and this saves you a lot of individual wiring.

You can also, if it suits, use one or more multi-plug bulkhead connectors to bring cables from the engine compartment inside the body. This has the convenience that if you want to take out something complete, you just unplug instead of having to undo lots of connections from a loom. It also makes it a lot easier to wire because you can do a complete panel or component on the bench and then just plug it into the car. If you find it difficult to get bulkhead connectors, try your nearest Rover dealer. Austin/Morris used them on several cars, and the dealer might still have some in stock or be able to get them for you. Alternatively, look for older Austin-Morris cars in a breakers.

There's one more point before I start getting busy with wire cutters and soldering iron, component earthing on a glass-fibre bodied kit car. Unlike the donor car which had a steel body, you can't earth through the component fixing screws, you've got to run separate earth cables. Rather than fixing individual earth cables all over the place on the steel chassis, use grouped earthing. By this, I mean pick several convenient earth points on the chassis and group the earth leads of the components near it to the one earth point. For components up to 6 watts you can use loop earthing in the same way as loop feeding, but for higher wattage components, use a separate earth lead for each. By far the best way of earthing is by ring connectors and a nut and bolt. You'll have to drill the chassis to take the bolts, but please be careful where you drill so that you don't weaken anything. Never drill holes in box sections or flanges of structural chassis members, nor into chassis members carrying steering, braking or suspension components. Good places to choose are gusset plates or body mounting plates.

Chapter 7

BRIGHT SPARKS

Engine running a shade rough? Starting not all it should be?

Chances are the ignition system needs an overhaul.

FAR TOO MANY KIT CAR OWNERS PUT UP WITH mediocre running of their engine because, in these days of no-maintenance electronic ignition, they've taken the sparks department for granted. They're classic cases of 'There's a spark at the plugs, so the ignition's all right' syndrome.

Part One
CONTACT BREAKER SYSTEMS

Let's look first at the older contact breaker system. Just about all modern ignitions are electronic but, if you're using an older donor car, don't necessarily despise the old contact breaker system. In good order and with reasonably regular maintenance it won't let you down. Spend some time, and a surprisingly small amount of money, on overhauling the distributor and you'll be delighted with the difference.

You can, if you want, go out and spend upwards of £85 on a new distributor, but the one I've illustrated here cost five quid at a breakers plus just under ten quid to overhaul it including a new cap, new rotor arm, new points and new capacitor. You can either overhaul the one that came with

First, check inside the cap. If the studs are badly burnt, get a new one but, if they're only discoloured, clean them with an fine-grade emery stick. Check that the centre button isn't worn.

your donor engine or, if you bought a bare engine, nip off to the nearest breakers and get yourself one.

A large number of kit cars use Ford engines so, to illustrate overhauling a contact breaker distributor, I decided on the Motorcraft one as probably the most popular because it's near enough the same on a Pinto and a Crossflow engine except that the one on the Pinto has a longer stalk on the drive. It's also very similar to the distributors fitted to other engines and the same overhaul principles apply except that the contact breaker points may not be a complete assembly, the fixed and moving points may be separate.

If they are, you can probably get a replacement assembly which fits the same as the later ones. If this fails, you may be able to get replacement points as a complete assembly as Lucas, AC Delco and a number of independent electrical companies made replacement points for most model Fords under their 'all makes' schemes. Most of these schemes started in the 1960s and 1970s and replacement points sets for older models are not often found in accessory shops. If you have an older model, try your Ford dealer first but, if he is unable to help, try the 'new old stock' dealers at autojumbles or the owners club for your model. If you are fitting separate points remember how the old ones came out and remember to fit the fibre washer between the fixed and moving points.

Next comes the rotor arm. Again, if the tip contact is burnt, get a new one. If it's just dirty, clean it with an emery stick.

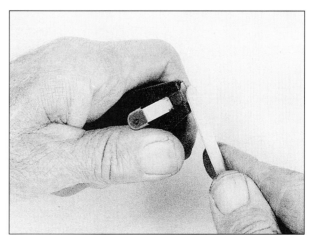

The centre contact isn't likely to be burnt unless its spring is weak so the spark had to jump. Clean off any discolouration.

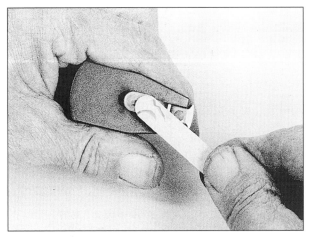

Upstairs now, don't waste time cleaning points, they're cheap so renew them. First undo the screw and slide out the two cables, one coming from the coil and one from the capacitor. On some Ford distributors you may find that the one from the coil goes via a radio suppressor.

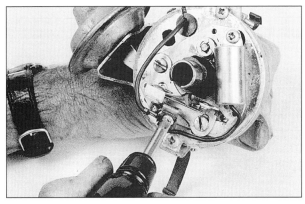

The points on the Motorcraft distributor lift away as a complete assembly, probably the simplest to renew of any make.

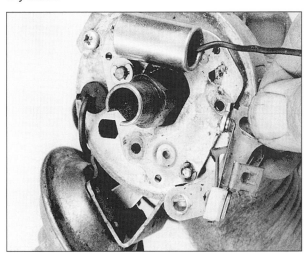

On the distributor body, the first check is the bottom bearing. If the drive gear can wobble, even slightly, reject it.

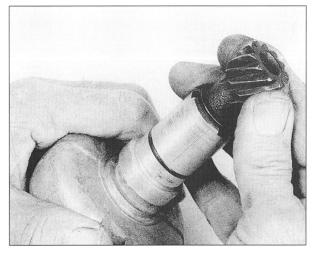

Then you can undo the two screws which hold the points to the baseplate.

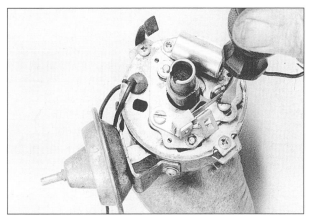

There isn't any easy way to check a capacitor but, if it's in poor nick your new points will burn. Capacitors are cheap, so get a new one. They vary in size, so take the old one with you.

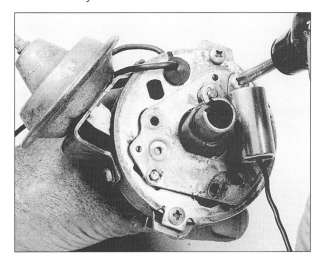

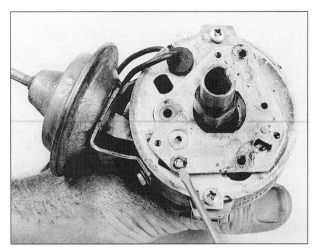

Before you can take the baseplate off you have to release the vacuum advance and retard rod. It's held by this small circlip. Below: The baseplate is held to the body by two screws, one each side.

Below: Once the screws are out, wriggle the baseplate free of the advance and retard rod and lift it off.

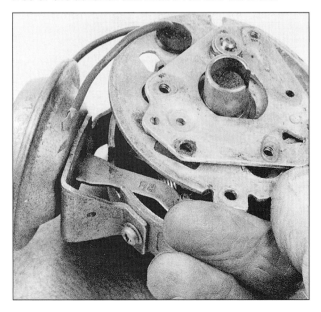

Under the baseplate you'll find the mechanical advance weights. Below: If you suspect the vacuum advance and retard unit of not working, or if it's damaged, take it off by undoing the two holding screws.

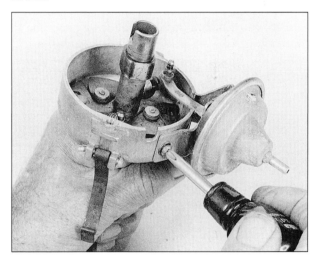

You can do a quick check on a vacuum advance and retard unit by putting your finger over the end and feeling for a puff when you work the rod back and forth.

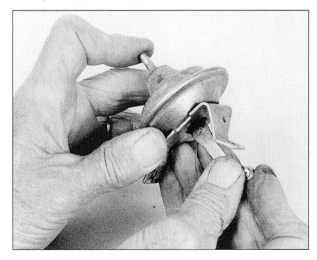

It's easy to forget and, if you do, the car won't start.

I hadn't got a Ford distributor to hand, at least not one that wanted overhauling, so I did the same as you would if you were looking for a spare distributor to overhaul. I went to my local breakers to see what I could find. There was a fair smattering of Cortinas and Mk2 Escorts in the yard, some still with the distributors in place, but I didn't just pick the first one I came to because I wanted a good one. I wasn't worried about the condition of the cap, rotor arm or points, but I rejected a couple without taking them off the engine because the cam plate, the bit that carries the rotor arm, had side shake where it had worn. They would never give a consistently good spark because the points gap would vary all over the place as the cam plate wobbled.

I rejected a third one after taking it out because the drive gear at the bottom had side shake where the bottom bearing

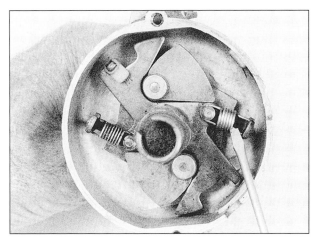

Above: These are the springs which control the mechanical advance. Notice that one is stronger than the other. The weaker one works at low revs, the stronger one at high revs. If you have to take them off because they're loose or bent, mark which weight takes the strong one. Below: There's a little plastic stop to limit the throw of the advance weights. If it's missing, the weights make a hell of a racket at high revs when they rub on the body sides.

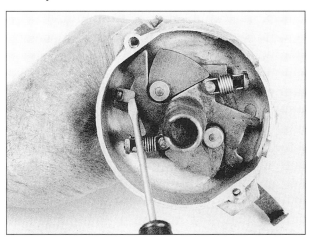

Above: You can alter the advance curve by bending the tags on to which the springs hook. Bend them outwards to increase the spring tension and decrease the rate of advance, or inwards to decrease the spring tension and increase the rate of advance. Lubricate the weights before you put the baseplate back.

Above: You can alter the advance curve after reassembly and testing by poking a stout screwdriver through the hole provided in the baseplate. Below: There should be a felt oil retaining pad inside the top of the cam plate.

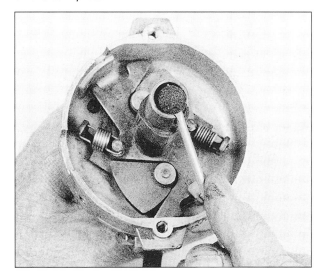

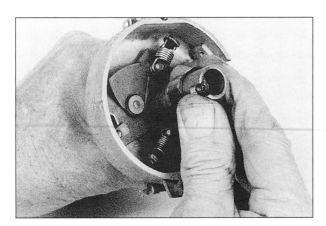

Test the cam plate for rock. If it can move sideways, it's worn and the points gap won't stay constant. On this model it's held by a circlip inside the top. On other models there may be a screw down inside to hold it. Below: When it's all together again, put just a light smear of grease on the cam faces.

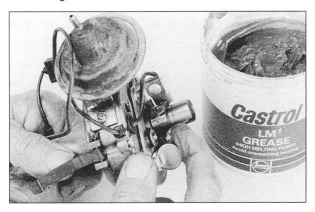

was worn. Then, perched on top of a Skoda I found a Mk2 Escort with its distributor still in place and smothered in black muck where the rocker cover had been leaking like a sieve. I was up to my elbows in grime by the time I got it out but, except for the cap which was a bit naff, there was practically no wear. The price? "A five-pun note to you, Squire."

While the distributor was soaking in a tub of white spirit to get rid of the grime, I took myself off to my local accessory shop and bought a new cap, new rotor arm, new points and new capacitor, all for just under £10. Follow the picture sequence to see how a total of fifteen quid produced an as-new distributor.

Part Two
ELECTRONIC IGNITION SYSTEMS

Now let's have a look at electronic ignition systems, fitted to most Fords since 1981. They're more reliable and efficient than the old contact breaker systems and, in some ways, they're more simple. Yet this very simplicity often makes them puzzling to the average kit car builder. Hit and miss checking

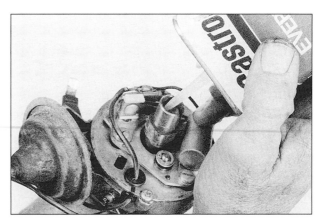

Last job of the overhaul is to drop some oil down the cam plate spindle and replace the felt pad, plus a few more drops of oil.

doesn't often find a problem unless you're very lucky, the easiest way is settle down to a spot of systematic checking. For most systems you don't need a lot of expensive equipment, just a decent quality meter and a test lamp.

I'm sticking to Ford systems because they're the most popular with kit cars and there isn't space in this book to cover all makes. If you're using a different donor, the general principles apply but you'll have to modify the checks after consulting the donor's workshop manual.

Before I start, a couple of words of warning. Modern electronic ignition systems generate far higher HT voltages than the old contact breaker systems. Don't try for HT lead sparking against the engine by holding the HT lead in your fingers. HT spark testing has its place in diagnosis, but hold the lead in a large pair of pliers with insulated handles. The second warning is that no-one with a heart pacemaker should test or work on electronic ignition systems. Even the magnetic fields round some programmed systems can affect a pacemaker and a high tension shock could be fatal.

One widely used, and probably the easiest system because it's so close in principle to the old contact breaker system, is the Bosch (or on some models Lucas) type with a constant energy amplifier. It's fitted to a large number of models and there are two types. On one, the amplifier is mounted on the side of the distributor body as in the CVH engined Fiesta 1.4; Escort and Orion 1.3, 1.4 and 1.6; XR3, XR3i; and Orion 1.6i.

On the second type, the amplifier is separate and may be mounted on the bulkhead or on the inner wing. This type is used on some Fiesta 1.1 and Escorts and Orions with the OHV engine; Cortina V6 2.0 and 2.3 from 1979 to 1982; Sierra 1.3, 1.6, 1.8, 2.0, 2.3 and 2.8i; Granada 1.6, 2.0, 2.3, 2.8 and 2.8i; and Capri 2.8i.

There isn't a lot you can do on overhauling the components, so let's get down to some trouble shooting. I'm assuming here that you've carried all the wiring over from the donor car so that checking should be exactly the same but, if all else fails, check your wiring connections again against the wiring diagram for the donor.

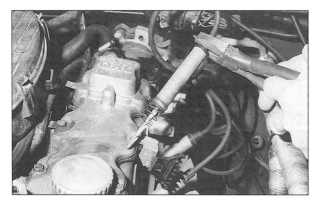

Above: Use a well insulated pair of pliers to hold an HT lead if you're checking the spark. Because of this car's long shroud, a suitable size drill bit can be used to make the contact. Below: Alternatively, you can buy visible spark plug indicators like this.

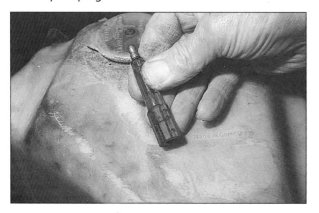

If you can't spot anything obviously wrong with the low tension leads, check for an HT spark. Get your heavily insulated pliers and hold one of the HT leads about a quarter of an inch from the engine block and get someone to crank the engine over. You should get a strong, blue, crackling spark. If you get nothing, or if the spark's yellow and very weak, you could have a fault with the leads, the coil or the distributor cap.

Check the leads for condition, check the distributor cap for cleanliness and possible signs of tracking (burnt paths between the towers, either inside or out) and check that the centre pick-up from the rotor is making good contact. Check the rotor arm for cracks or tracking. For the coil, you need to get your meter out. Switch the ignition on and check the voltage at the positive low-tension terminal of the coil. This system doesn't use a ballast resistor so you should get battery voltage. If you don't, check the wiring to the ignition coil and the ignition switch.

If you get battery voltage, switch off, disconnect both low tension leads from the coil and use your meter to check the resistance between the two terminals, the resistance of the primary coil. It should be quite low, about 0.7 to 0.8 ohms. If you get a high resistance, or an infinity reading which indicates an open circuit, the coil's had it. Assuming the

primary checked out OK then, if your meter will cover it, measure the resistance between one of the low tension terminals, it doesn't matter which, and the HT terminal inside the tower. This should be between 4,500 and 7,000 ohms. If you get readings widely outside these figures, try borrowing another coil.

If everything's in order so far, switch the ignition off, take the two low tension cables off the coil and connect a 12 volt test lamp between them. Get someone to crank the engine and the lamp should flash as the low tension circuit is made and broken.

If the lamp doesn't flash, you've got a fault either in the distributor, which is relatively rare or, more likely, in the amplifier. Amplifiers are notorious for packing up if they get too hot inside, and they get too hot because the body isn't making good contact with whatever it's bolted to, either the car body or the distributor body. If you have to fit a new amplifier, or a secondhand one for that matter, make sure the base is clean, make sure the area where it's going to make contact is clean, and smear the bolting faces with heat conducting paste which you can get from a Ford main dealer.

Now let's move on to the programmed systems. There's the Ford ESC fitted to Fiesta 1.3 CVH, XR2 and RS Turbo. Second,

Above: Here you can see how the spark plug tester connects in between the HT lead and the spark plug. A light flashes every time the spark is made. Below: Measuring the resistance of the coil's primary windings. In this case, 3.3 ohms is far too high, and the coil was failing at high revs because of its long recuperation time.

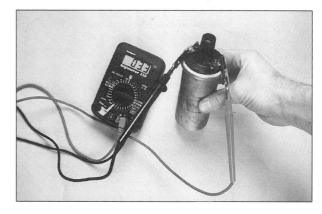

we have the Lucas programmed system fitted to Sierra 1.6 from 1982 to 1984 and third, Ford's programmed system with a single crank angle sensor fitted to Sierra 1.8 from 1988.

On the ESC system you can carry out all the checks the same as with the Bosch system. On the Lucas programmed system the checks are similar except that you mustn't use the flashing test lamp on the coil's low tension leads. There are extra checks on the Lucas amplifier module. This differs from the previous amplifiers in that it also controls the automatic advance and retard instead of leaving it to the distributor. If the advance and retard function fails in the module, it will automatically set the ignition timing retarded so that the car can be driven home or to a dealer but you will be very much down on power.

You can do a preliminary check with a strobe lamp to check that the ignition advances as the engine is speeded up from idle, but to make sure the fault is in the module you need a vacuum pump which is connected to the ESC unit in place of the pipe from the inlet manifold. With the engine ticking over, the ignition should advance, as shown on a strobe light, when vacuum is applied without the engine speed increasing. Any dealer can make this simple check for you.

Quite common on this system are faults because of bad connections. Typical are a bad connection of the feed to the module - you should get battery voltage between pins 2 and 9 of the harness when you disconnect it from the ESC and switch the ignition on. Pin 2 is the battery voltage feed and pin 9 should be connected to earth. Also check all the connections at the distributor.

The coil checks on Ford's single crank angle sensor system are the same as on the Bosch system except that, like the Lucas system, the flashing lamp test shouldn't be used. Bad connections are also responsible for many faults with this system. you can check the voltage at the wiring harness to the ECU in a similar way to the Lucas module except that, in this case, pin 10 should give battery voltage and pin 9 is connected to earth.

There is also an octane compensation plug on this system, located near the coil. You can get a special service harness to plug into this with wires that can be earthed to retard the ignition. To run on 95 octane unleaded, the blue wire should be earthed. This earths terminal 25 on the ECU and retards the ignition. If you are running on 91 octane, the red wire should be earthed which has the effect of earthing terminal 24 on the ECU to give further advance. If you still get pinking with either of these wires earthed, you can earth both of them which will retard the ignition still further but will cut down quite a lot on power. It's worthwhile, on a secondhand car, checking what the position is if you're down on power.

A system very much on its own is Ford's DIS or Distributorless Ignition System. This is the one where, naturally,

Checking the resistance of the coil's secondary windings. In this case it just about scraped through.

you don't have a distributor but you have a large black coil component on the bulkhead with the four HT leads coming from it. This system is fitted to Escort 1.1 and 1.3 and Orion 1.3 from 1988.

On this system you can check the coil in a similar way to the previous systems but, because it's a double coil, you have two low tension readings to take. When you take off the low tension connector plug at the coil you have three connections, a central positive one and two outer negative ones. Check for battery voltage from the centre connection to each of the outer ones in turn. Checking the primary resistance of the coil is similar, check with the meter between the centre low tension terminal on the coil and each of the outer ones. You should get a low resistance of around 0.5 ohms. To check the secondary resistance, remove the HT leads and connect your meter across each pair of HT terminals. You should get a reading of between 1100 and 1600 ohms. These coils sometimes fail if they overheat, and this is usually caused by a bad physical connection to the bulkhead so the heat can't escape.

In place of the distributor there is a crank sensor and these occasionally fail. Disconnect the wiring harness to it and check across the terminals of the sensor for continuity. You also have a coolant temperature sensor in the manifold at the back behind the air cleaner and an air temperature sensor in the base of the air cleaner. If either of these fails, the ECU will assume that either the engine is running too hot or that the air intake temperature is too hot and will, in each case, retard the ignition. You can still drive the car, but your power will be down.

Now we come to the two types of integrated fuel and ignition systems. The first group are the EEC IV, ESC II or Motorcraft TFI V systems fitted to Sierra 1.8, 2.0, 2.0i and Granada/Scorpio 1.8, 2.0, 2.8i and 2.9i. On these systems, which are very similar, you can carry out the coil low tension and high tension checks as with the Bosch system I first mentioned, including the flashing lamp test, and check all the harness connections for cleanliness and security, but I wouldn't advise any meter testing on the electronic module itself as it can be easily damaged by the internal battery of your meter.

Lastly, there's the Weber/Marelli integrated fuel and ignition system in the RS Cosworth and Sapphire. Here, I wouldn't advise any checking other than the primary and secondary resistance checks on the coil and making sure that all the connections are good. The ECU on this system is very sensitive to meter voltages and could easily be damaged if you aren't 100 per cent certain what you're doing.

Part Three
UPGRADING A CROSSFLOW TO ELECTRONIC IGNITION

Ford's Crossflow engine is still very popular for kit cars, and a good reliable lump it is too. What's more it responds very well to a spot of upgrading on the ignition system.

You can equip your Crossflow with electronic ignition, and I mean electronic, not one of the halfway house type that still use the points, without digging too deep and going without food for a week to pay for it.

Ford went over to electronic ignition round about 1981 on the Escort, and most people think that they did it only on the CVH engine. But they didn't do it only on that. The MkIV 1300 Escort's got a very nice Bosch electronic ignition. Not on a CVH engine, but on a Valencia engine which is very similar to the Crossflow fitted to MkI and MkII Escorts, Cortinas, Capris and a few others.

What's nice from our point of view is that the distributor from the Valencia will drop straight in to the Crossflow so that, with a few minor wiring alterations and a change of coil you've got yourself a reliable electronic set-up. You can buy all the bits from a Ford main dealer if you want to, or you can

Get yourself a Bosch electronic distributor from a Valencia engine and it will drop straight into your Crossflow.

save a lot of dosh by going for a hunt round a breakers yard. Interested? Thought you would be.

If you've bought your Bosch distributor new you can go ahead and fit it straight in but, if you're buying it from a breakers, you should make a few checks before you part with your cash, and do a spot of maintenance when you get home. The checks first of all. The distributor as it comes from the Valencia engine will be fitted with a top entry cap. If you intend using it with this cap, do the usual checks. Take a look inside and check that the studs aren't burnt and that there's no sign of tracking between them. The HT voltage is higher than a distributor with contact breaker points and any tracking will soon develop into a burnt out and ruined cap.

However, there isn't all that much room on a Crossflow for the top entry cap, particularly if you've got a modified inlet manifold, so you may be better off with a new side entry cap. Bosch do one, but I'll tell you how to get one much cheaper than the Bosch one in a moment.

After taking the cap off, lift the rotor arm and the dust shield and watch the gaps between the four-star trigger wheel and the four stator arms. They should be as near as makes no difference the same and there shouldn't be any wobble on the trigger wheel shaft. If there is, put it down and look for a less worn one. The actual gap should be about 0.012in, that's about 0.30mm, but it isn't all that critical.

The second check concerns the amplifier module on the side of the distributor body. You often find people complaining that these have given up the ghost and that they don't last very long. They don't, if you don't fit them properly. They do if you do fit them properly.

When the amplifier modules fail they nearly always do so because they've been overheated. The main way the module gets rid of its heat is to the body of the distributor, so it must make good, clean contact. If it makes poor contact it will overheat and burn out. Take it off - it's held by two screws - and clean both mating surfaces thoroughly. It doesn't hurt to bring the body of the distributor up bright with a piece of emery cloth. Then coat both faces liberally with the special

You also need the multi-plug and lead that goes with the Bosch distributor.

The gap between the trigger wheel arms and the stator arms should be about 0.012in, and the trigger wheel mustn't rock or wobble.

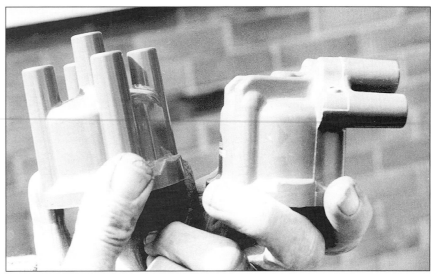

If things are tight with the top entry cap (left), you can get a cheap side entry cap from the Motorcraft catalogue - but it's listed for a Fiat.

heat conducting compound which you can buy at Ford main dealers, and screw the amplifier back on. This same tip, as I mentioned earlier, applies to distributors on CVH engines as well.

Assuming everything's now OK, you're ready to drop it in. Before you do, turn the engine till no.1 cylinder is on compression (both rocker arms have clearance because both valves should be closed) and stop at top dead centre which is marked on the crankshaft pulley.

Look carefully round the rim of the distributor body and you'll find a notch. Put the rotor arm on and turn the cog at the bottom till the rotor's pointing at this notch and the arms of the trigger wheel are opposite the stator arms. That's the firing position for number 1 cylinder - the front one on a Crossflow. Now fit the clamping plate from your old Motorcraft distributor because the one from the Valencia won't fit your engine.

There's a little dodge to dropping the distributor in which you'll find useful. The distributor is driven by a skew gear on the camshaft which means that the centre shaft and trigger wheel turn as you feed it in. Feed it in starting with the rotor pointing towards the notch, watch by how much it turns and make a pencil mark on the rim opposite where the rotor

This is why most amplifiers fail. There must be good heat contact with the distributor body.

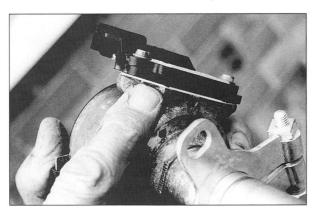

stops. Now go back the other side of the notch and make another pencil mark the same distance away on the other side. Pull the distributor out again and start with the rotor pointing to your second pencil mark. This time when you feed it in, the rotor should stop opposite the notch. If it's just a shade out, slacken the clamping plate and turn the distributor body till the trigger wheel arms are lined up with the stator arms.

You're now at no.1 cylinder firing position and, when you fit the cap, the rotor will be pointing at the stud for the HT lead to No.1 cylinder. If you've forgotten where the other leads go, remember that the distributor turns anti-clockwise looking at the top and the firing order for a Crossflow is 1-2-4-3.

Oh yes, I said I'd tell you where to get a cheap side entry distributor cap. The Bosch one is quite expensive, but there's an equally good and very much cheaper one in Ford's Motorcraft any-makes catalogue. It's listed for a Fiat Strada Super 75 and 85 and its Motorcraft part number is 5005566. It fits the Bosch distributor perfectly.

Right, you're almost ready to go, but not quite. You've got a few wiring changes to make. First of all, your coil, if you got it from a donor Ford that had a Crossflow engine, will be a ballasted one designed to run at 9 volts. This doesn't suit your new distributor, so you want an unballasted one running at 12 volts. The standard coil from any Escort fitted with a CVH engine is one that will do. To use it, you've got to replace the ballast lead which fed the low voltage to the coil with a plain cable running from the ignition switch down to the positive side of the 12 volt coil.

You also need the multi-plug lead which goes with the Bosch distributor, either a new one from a Ford dealer or the one that was fitted to the coil you got from a breakers. This has three cables in it, brown, green and black.

The green cable goes to the positive side of the coil, the same terminal where you fitted your 12 volt feed cable from the ignition switch. The black cable goes to the other low tension terminal on the coil, the negative side. This is the terminal which also feeds the electric rev counter if you've got one fitted. The third cable, the brown one, goes to chassis earth.

Now you're all ready. You're timed accurately enough to get the engine running so switch on and fire up and check your ignition timing with a strobe lamp. Disconnect the vacuum capsule on the distributor and plug the end that goes to the inlet manifold. Then time the distributor to between 8 and 9 degrees before TDC at tick-over - about 850 to 900 rpm - as a good starting point. This will probably suit your Crossflow if it's got a standard camshaft but, if you've fitted a performance shaft, you may find that any setting between 6 degrees before TDC and 11 degrees before TDC suits it better.

The ideal way to check it is to have a session on a rolling road and have the advance curve plotted, but this is quite expensive. I usually try things out on the road and make adjustments a degree or two at a time to see how it behaves. I advance it till I just get pinking on hard acceleration, then back it off a degree or so till I don't. It's not very scientific, but with a bit of practice you can get it pretty close to optimum.

If you're looking for top power, a rolling road session is essential and you may be told that the advance curve isn't the best possible for a Crossflow. That's because it was designed for a Valencia, but I know of several 1600 Escorts tuned to be pretty hot stuff which are running with the Valencia distributor in standard trim and they're certainly no slouches. If you're really worried about it, any rolling road man who knows his stuff can probably modify the curve for you with a different vacuum advance capsule but, personally, I wouldn't bother.

Part Four
HT LEADS & PLUGS

It's all very well having the coil and distributor in apple pie order, or all three connections on an electronic system clean and tight, but you still won't get what all the rest of the system is designed to do - get a good spark at the plugs - if the HT leads are old and leaking. Don't trust the old leads that came with the donor car, even if they look fine. For the relatively small cost of a new set, make sure about things.

However, like most things in life, fitting a new set of HT leads isn't quite so simple as it sounds. You can go to an accessory shop and buy a complete set of leads quite cheaply which are labelled as suitable for your engine, and the engine will run with them. But it may not, probably not, run as well or as economically as it should. On the other hand, you can go and buy a really expensive set of leads which may or may not be best for your engine. So how do you decide?

Basically there are four types of HT leads. First, you get the old-fashioned straight length of copper wire inside an insulated sleeve with plain caps on the ends for the distributor and the plugs. They have quite a low resistance so they don't delay the release of the spark energy from the coil. Generally speaking, which is always a dangerous thing to do, these leads like a fairly large plug gap rather than a small one. They also set up horrible radio and TV interference which is why it's illegal to use them on the road.

Next, you get a variation on the plain lead but the end caps for the distributor and the plugs have resistors in them, typically 1 KΩ (kilo-ohm) at the distributor and 5 KΩ at the plugs. These are probably the lowest resistance leads with suppression you can get.

The third type covers most original equipment leads and most of the better ones you buy at dealers and in accessory shops. These have a carbon filament core instead of a copper wire and the suppression resistance runs the whole length of the lead with no added resistance in the end caps. Typically, their resistance in between 10 and 15 KΩ per metre.

Lastly we get the wire wound type of lead where the conductor through the centre is made up of coils of wire wound on what's generally called the 'tight-loose' principle which means that one coil is wound tight and close and the other is wound wider and looser. NGK leads, now no longer available on the aftermarket, were examples of this type of construction and you could see the coils because the insulating sleeve was semi-transparent. Most coil-wound leads made by other makers have opaque insulation so, from looking, you can't tell the difference between those and carbon filament leads. These are lower resistance than carbon filament, typically 7 to 8 KΩ per metre.

I wish I could give you a plain straightforward answer about which type you should fit, but I can't. No-one can, though different makers of leads will naturally tell you that their particular type of construction is best.

Once again generally speaking, changing the resistance in the leads changes the duration of the spark. With a low resistance HT lead the spark energy in the coil is released more quickly so you get a shorter, sharper spark. With a higher resistance lead the voltage flow, to use a very unscientific term, is slowed along the lead so you get a longer duration spark.

The plug gap also affects the spark voltage. When the coil releases its energy, and it doesn't matter here whether we're talking about electronic or points ignition, the voltage builds up until it's big enough to jump the gap at the plug. It follows that, if you increase the gap there is a longer delay, so a big gap gives you a higher voltage spark. There is, however, a limit, because if the gap is too big the coil won't be able to produce enough energy for the spark to jump across.

The ability of the spark to jump the gap is also affected by the conditions inside the combustion chamber. The higher the compression, the harder it is for the spark to jump, and it's also affected by the air/fuel mixture round the plug. This is why you can often have a larger plug gap with fuel injection than with a carburetted engine with poor atomisation and swirl.

What it all boils down to is that, with a tuned engine, the ideal is to aim for the best choice of HT lead and plug gap that suits your particular set-up. The only way to do this properly is on a rolling road linked to a sophisticated electronic tester that can tell you whether a misfire or drop in power at high revs is due to fuelling or spark. Sometimes, changing the resistance of the HT leads or changing the size of the plug gap can cure a high-speed misfire or fill in a dip in the power curve quite dramatically.

I've assumed here, of course, that the leads, the distributor cap, the rotor arm and the plugs are in top-line condition. HT leads do age, and the spark energy can leak through the insulation, but none of the ignition experts I spoke to came up with any way of judging by looking at them whether or not a set of leads was likely to leak or not unless they were obviously cracked and flaking. Sometimes, on a dark, damp night you can see a blue haze hovering over leads that are leaking, but once again, a rolling road test with an electronic computer read out of the ignition condition is best.

Distributor caps and rotor arms can have a surprising effect on spark intensity. Every time the spark has to jump a gap it looses energy. If the connections inside the towers on the distributor cap or coil are corroded, the spark has to jump this corrosion, and this burns the connection so you get a vicious circle of lost energy. The same thing applies where the contact from the top of the cap meets the rotor arm and where the spark has to jump the gap between the end of the rotor arm and the plug lead studs. You're bound to get burning at this gap, and most people clean it off with a piece of emery paper or a file, but this makes the gap larger,

It's no good having the coil and distributor in tip top condition if you can't get a decent spark to the plugs. The condition of HT leads is often overlooked.

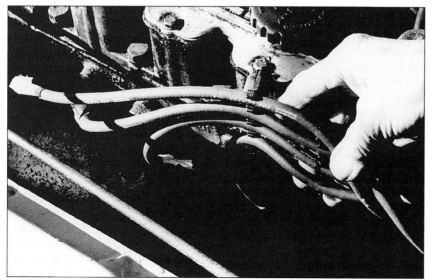

which also looses energy. This is why, if you're looking for top power, it pays to renew the distributor cap at least once every second time you renew the plugs.

Which brings us, quite neatly, to the plugs. All too often, we don't give the humble sparking plug the attention it deserves.

Probably that's because modern plugs are so reliable even though they work pretty hard for their living. At 6,000 rpm a plug has to produce a spark 3,000 times a minute, or 50 times a second, which doesn't leave a lot of room for misbehaviour. What's more, each time it sparks it's exposed to searing hot burning gases, and a fiftieth of a second isn't very long for that heat to get away from the points.

Most of us have an idea, even if it's a rough idea, about 'hot' and 'cold' plugs and we realise that if the heat doesn't get away from the tip of the plug fast enough we can get misfiring. So we might look at a maker's chart and make sure we fit a plug of the right heat range but, more often than not, we go to an accessory shop and ask for a set of plugs for a particular engine and fit whatever the sales assistant gives us.

But should we pay a lot more attention to buying plugs? As much attention, for example, as we would to buying a new camshaft? Plug makers say we should, so let's take a look at the things we should take into account when we choose a plug.

First there's the reach, usually taken to mean the length of the threaded bit. Flat seat plugs, the ones you fit with copper washers under them, come with standard reaches of 3/8in, 1/2in and 3/4in. Taper seat plugs come in standard short and long reaches, 0.460in and 0.708in. There ought not to be any mistake but, on occasions, we've come across short reach plugs fitted in long reach heads which means that the last few threads in the head get carboned up and you have to use a tap to clean them out before the proper reach plug will screw in. Less likely, because it often means that the plug hits the piston, is a long reach plug fitted in short reach head.

Heat conductivity, the speed at which the heat moves away from the points to the body and then into the head, varies according to whether the plug is 'hot' or 'cold' running. Hot plugs are fitted in engines where the temperature is lower, usually lower performance engines and, conversely, cold plugs are fitted in hotter engines, usually tuned engines.

If your plugs tend to foul up on long periods of tickover, or if they misfire with long bursts of power, you might possibly need a plug one or two grades up or down the heat range. Check with the plug maker to find out. Heat conductivity is improved by having a centre electrode with a copper core and most modern cold plugs have this.

Some plugs have also got resistors built in to the centre electrode to cut down on radio interference. There's a slight reduction in discharge current, but not enough to worry about. Used together with resistive plug leads they can make quite a difference to interference on modern very sensitive hi-fi radios and tape or CD players.

You'll also find that some plugs have the nose of the centre insulator sticking out more than others. The idea of this is that the nose is exposed to the cooling charge of incoming air and fuel which helps to prevent it getting too hot. It does but, before you rush out to buy these, check that there isn't going to be a foul between the nose of the plug and the piston particularly if you're running high compression where clearances can get a little on the tight side.

OK, now we come to the bit that's usually pushed in the adverts, the special patented designs of points that are claimed to give you better performance, better fuel consumption, lower emissions and all the rest of the desirable benefits of better ignition. What's the theory behind them?

They're all based on two things, giving a nice fat spark to start the ignition process quickly, and exposing the spark directly to the fuel and air mixture.

If you're in to racing engines you'll have heard about indexing a plug. This is making sure that, when a plug is screwed right home in the head, the open end of the points faces the incoming fuel and air charge. If the closed, or back end of the points faces the charge, the gas has to find its way round there before ignition can begin. I'm talking about very small fractions of a second but, at the very high revs of racing engines, small fractions of a second in ignition can make a lot of difference.

It isn't worth going to all the trouble of indexing plugs on normal fast road engines, the usual practice both with contact breaker ignition and the type of electronic ignition that still uses a coil, is to fit a high discharge coil and open up the plug points gap to get a big spark. With full electronic mapped ignition, the voltage is usually higher than with a coil so a bigger plug points gap is usually specified.

Two plug makers however, Nippondenso and Splitfire, claim that they've found the answer by putting a groove in the earth electrode of the plug but they do it in different ways.

Nippondenso put their groove along the earth electrode so that it looks like a small channel. The claim is that this results in a larger spark than with a conventional flat electrode.

Splitfire as the name suggests, put a split groove in the end of their earth electrode. The claim here is again a bigger spark with better combustion and their claims seem to be backed up by tests in the US by Ford, Chrysler and GM. I've heard conflicting reports from engine tuners about the effectiveness of these plugs. Some say they like them, while others say that they don't last very long before they start to give misfires at high revs. If you fancy trying them, the best advice I can give is to go ahead. They won't harm the engine and, if you start to get misfiring or other loss of performance at high revs, you can always switch back to conventional plugs.

With conventional plugs for a road engine, the best advice is to fit a reputable well-known make and make sure you get the heat range right. If you're going in for racing, there's a lot more plug technology which you might like to investigate, like using exotic metals for the electrodes, multiple earth electrodes, or even no earth electrode at all with the spark jumping straight to the body. I haven't got room here to go into them all, but you can get brochures and literature from all the makers and judge for yourself.

Chapter 8

WHAT THE LAW REQUIRES

You can't just bolt lamps on any old where. The law lays down certain requirements you must observe.

THE KIT MANUFACTURER SHOULD BE WELL AWARE OF the legal positioning of obligatory lights, the ones the law says you must have, but it's as well to know what the law is so that you aren't caught out when you take your car for Single Vehicle Approval.

The lamps you must have are two headlamps, two front sidelamps, or marker lamps as they are sometimes called, two rear marker lamps, two brake stop lamps, a rear number plate lamp and front and rear indicator lamps. You can, if you want, add side repeater indicator lamps. They aren't a legal requirement but, if they're fitted, they must be working. You must also have two rearward facing red reflectors at the back of the car.

How to wire driving lamps using a four-connection relay. Fog lamps are wired similarly except that the feed to the switch is tapped into the sidelamp circuit.

Now for positions. The front sidelamps must not be more than 400mm from the outside edge of the car, and the outside edge is taken as the outside of the bodywork, not any external mirrors. There isn't a position given for the minimum or maximum height, but use your loaf and don't put them right down next to the ground. Remember that they are there so that other drivers can see the width of your car at night, so put them where they're readily visible. They must also be visible from the side of the car, by a person standing level with the lamps at an angle of 90 degrees to the centreline of the car.

Rear sidelamps must also be within 400mm from the outside edge of the car, but here there is also a minimum height of 350mm from the ground. The same applies to brake stop lamps, rear indicators and rear reflectors, which is why they are often incorporated in a single lamp cluster. The rear lamps, brake lamps, indicators and reflectors must be matched pairs and each pair must be an equal distance from the centreline of the car. There isn't a legal position laid down for the rear number plate lamp, but it must illuminate the number plate and come on when the sidelamps and rear lamps are switched on. Like the sidelamps, the rear lamps and indicators must be visible to a person standing level with them at the side of the car.

At the front, there isn't a laid down position for main beam headlamps, but there is for dipped beam. Once again, they must be a matched pair, the same distance each side of the car's centreline, and not more than 400mm from the outside edge of the car. The minimum height is 500mm. All minimum heights are measured from the lowest part of the illuminated area. For the dipped beam that is taken to be where the apparent trace of the beam 'cut-off' can be seen on the lens. The same regulations about the position of the rear indicators also apply to the front ones. You also have to watch the law when you fit extra lamps which aren't a legal

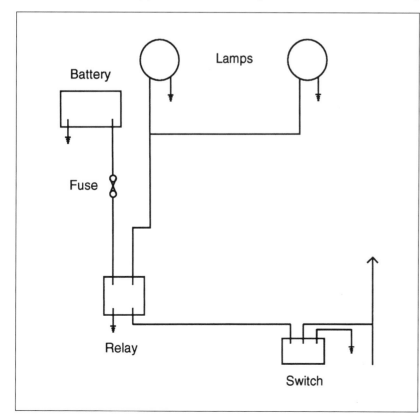

requirement. First, extra front driving lamps. There are two things to keep in mind here. The first is that the lamps must be equally spaced either side of the car's centre line and the second is that the switching must be arranged so that they can be used only when the headlights are on full beam. The first is easy enough to comply with and, if you look at the lighting schematic in Chapter 6 you'll see that this is how I've arranged the switching to the relay.

With front fog lights there's no legal requirement about how they're switched but the usual arrangement is that they're switched to come on only when the sidelights are on, mainly so that you don't have them on accidentally in bright daylight, and this is also how I've arranged them in the schematic. There are, however, regulations about how high or low you can fit them and how far in from the outside of the car they must be. Most people fit twin front fog lights and, like driving lamps, they should be equally spaced either side of the car's centre line. Also, the outside edge of each lamp must not be more than 400mm from the outside edge of the car.

There's a height restriction too, which says that the top edges of the lamps must not be more than 1200mm from the ground. Most people like to fit them below the bumper to avoid as much glare back from the fog as possible but, if you've got a front air dam skirt that

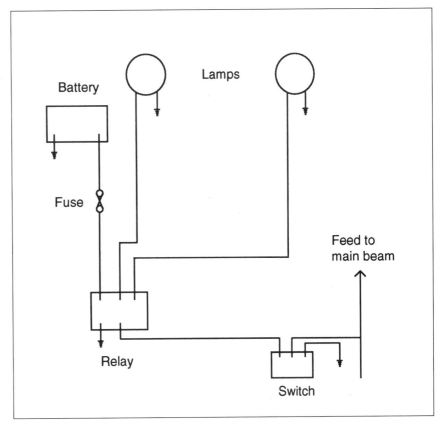

If you use a five-connection relay you can take separate cables to each driving lamp so you can use a lighter cable.

makes this awkward, a maximum height of 1200mm gives you bags of leeway to fit them above the bumper. Fog lamps can be on while the headlights are on dipped beam and they have to be aimed so they don't cause

Column stalks can be a good way of avoiding endless dash mounted switches which may not always pass the SVA's internal projections test. If nothing else, column stalks are far more handy to use.

If you must fit dash mounted switches, these rocker switches are far more likely to pass the SVA test than the more traditional toggle type ones.

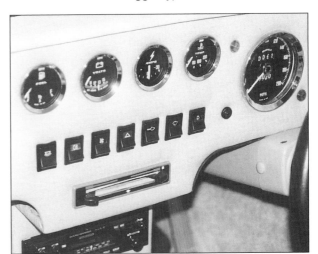

Above: Using a donor car's rear light cluster can be a good way of ensuring you have all the necessary lighting positioned in the right place. Below: Here are the required lighting positions for all lamps.

OBLIGATORY LAMPS		
	Max dist. from side	Min Height
Dipped Beam	400mm	500mm
Main Beam	–	–
Front side lamps	400mm	–
Rear side lamps	400mm	350mm
Rear registration light	–	–
Stop lamps	400mm apart	350mm
Rear fog lamp	250mm	–
Indicators (front, sides & rears)	400mm	350mm
Rear retro reflectors	400mm	350mm

dazzle to other road users. Unlike headlights, there isn't a beam-setting requirement so whether or not fog lamps dazzle is left to the opinion of an MoT examiner or the police.

Moving round to the back of the car, to rear fog lamps, owners usually fit these in pairs but there's no legal requirement to do so in the UK. However, if you fit two they must be a matched pair, and you are not allowed to fit more than two. If you fit just one it must be to the right of the car's centre line so you can, if you want, balance it on the other side with a reversing lamp if your car hasn't already got one. The only problem with this arrangement is that if you take your car to the Continent the single rear fog lamp will be illegal because it will be on the wrong side of the car.

There are also regulations about height. The bottom edge of the lamp must be at least 250mm from the ground and the top edge mustn't be more than 1000mm from the ground which, again, gives you quite a lot of

leeway. Anyone behind you while you've got your rear fog lamps on must be able to see easily when your brake lights come on, and the regulations say that the outside edge of the rear fog lamp must be at least 100mm inboard of the inside edge of the brake lamp. There must be a warning (tell-tale) light on the dash that rear fog lamps are switched on (also for main beam).

There aren't any regulations about where you position a reversing lamp, but you mustn't fit more than two, and while you are actually reversing is the only time you are allowed to show a white light at the back of your car. Reversing lamps must be switched either so that they come on only when the gear lever is in reverse, usually by a switch on the gearbox or, if they're controlled by a switch on the dashboard, there must be a warning light to remind the driver that they're switched on.

Some people like to fit a pair of extra brake lights in the rear window but often don't realise that there are regulations covering these, too. The bottom edge of the lamps must be at least 400mm from the ground and the top edge not more than 1500mm from the ground. There must also be a minimum of 600mm between the inside edges of the lamps. They must be used only for indication of braking and must operate only when the car's other brake lights come on.

All the extra lamps you fit must be E-marked as being approved for their particular use and, though it isn't a legal requirement for them to be fitted, if they are fitted they must work unless they are covered up or not connected to the electrical system.

Whilst we're talking about the legal aspects of wiring etc, let's not forget another area that will be increasingly important if your kit has to go through Single Vehicle Approval. Whilst light heights are the most obvious area where you may come unstuck, using the correct types of switches inside the car may also be important. With the introduction of Single Vehicle Approval (which was coming into force as this book was written) you'll also have to think about internal protrusions in the cockpit.

Whilst this covers a number of features inside your cabin, it may also affect the type of switches you use. Traditional toggle switches may only be fitted on the dash if they are behind the steering wheel, and therefore hidden from the occupant in the event of a front end smash. Keeping this in mind, you may want to avoid unnecessary switches altogether, when column mounted stalk controls can do the same job. So, it's worth thinking about these things before you plump for something that looks great but may not actually be legal.

Chapter 9

STARTER TROUBLE

Even the best kit car isn't a lot of good if it won't start, but don't despair,

a spot of logical checking will soon sort things out.

Part One
PINPOINTING THE FAULT

I'LL DEAL WITH OVERHAULING STARTER MOTORS IN A moment but, first, I want to go over the checks to make when the engine won't turn over fast enough to start or, possibly more frustrating, when all you get when you turn the key is a deafening silence or a despairing and dying gurrrr.

In the case of the deafening silence, look at the ignition and oil warning lights. If they stay bright and clear when you turn the key, something's not quite right in the circuit that energises the starter solenoid and the starter isn't even trying to get current.

The warning lights came on when you switched on the ignition, so you're safe in assuming that you've got current getting to the key switch, so the first thing to check is that current is going out again to the solenoid

Test 1. If the starter turns, but is very sluggish, check the voltage across the battery while a helper turns the key. You'll get a drop, but it should be at least 9 to 9.5 volts. If it's less, it could be the starter, the battery, the solenoid or a bad connection. Carry on to find out where the fault is.

when you turn the key to 'Start'.

The feed out of the switch will go either to a relay or direct to the solenoid, depending on the wiring of your donor car. Check first at the switch and then at the other end of the cable to make sure you're getting the 12 volts you ought to. If you're getting 9 or so volts instead of 12, you've got the ballast ignition resistance cable and the solenoid cable mixed up. I've known it happen. Check and make sure.

If you're getting your 12 volts (or near enough, like 11.6 or something), and you've got a relay, check this out next. If it clicks just once when you turn the key to 'Start', it's probably OK. If it continues to click like a woodpecker it probably isn't, but in either case get the meter and check to make sure.

There are so many different kinds and shapes of relay that I can't give you specific terminals to check, but if you think back to earlier in this book and look at the wiring diagram for the donor car you'll see that there are four terminals on the relay, two for the energising circuit and two for the switching circuit.

The feed from the ignition switch will go to one of the energising circuit terminals. The other energising terminal will go to earth. If the relay doesn't click at all when you switch to 'Start', either the internal contacts are broken or the second cable isn't making good earth contact. Use your meter to check the resistance between the second terminal of the energising circuit and a clean part of the chassis. It should be zero ohms. If you've got a continuity check on your meter you can use that instead of the resistance setting.

If that's OK, look at the other two terminals, the switching circuit. One of them should be live all the time, so check with your meter set to read volts. If you're getting voltage to one switching terminal, take the cable off the other one, turn the key to 'Start', and check that you get 12 volts at the second switching terminal. If you do, the relay's OK. The cable you took off goes to the starter solenoid, so put it back on the

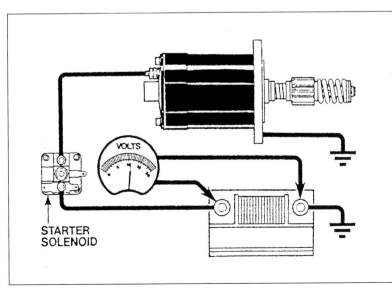

VOLTS

STARTER
SOLENOID

relay, take the other end off the solenoid and again switch to 'Start'. Check that you're getting 12 volts at the end of the cable. If that's OK, you've checked out the relay circuit so we can move on to the main heavy-current starter circuit.

Now let's take the other case and assume that when you turned the key the ignition and oil warning lights on the dash went out indicating that the starter circuit is trying to take everything the battery can give. The first thing to check is that the battery's got what it takes to give.

I don't care if you had the battery on charge for a week, never assume that it's fully charged. Even if the meter indicates a full 12 volts when you put the probes across the battery terminals it's no guarantee that all's well within the battery. It might be shorting out internally under load.

Invariably, this is because one of the cells is on its way out and, as I mentioned earlier, the only way to check for this is with a hydrometer which checks the specific gravity of the electrolyte in the battery. With a fully charged cell the reading ought to be within 1.270 and 1.290. A reading between 1.230 and 1.250 indicates about 70% charged, which is about as low as you want to go for reliable starting. A reading right down between 1.110 and 1.130 means it's as flat as a pancake.

What often happens is that you'll get a good reading from five of the cells and a rotten reading from one. If this happens then sorry, but the battery's had it. It just

Test 2. Check the voltage at the starter under load. It shouldn't be more than 0.5 volts below that recorded at the battery under load. If it is, it indicates a high resistance somewhere between the two.

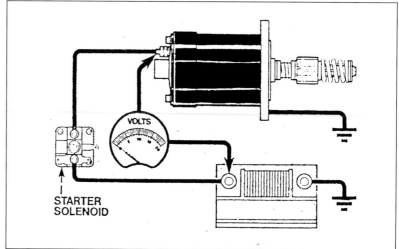

Test 3. This checks for a high resistance. When cranking the engine over, the voltage should be nearly zero. If it's high, move to test 4.

won't cope with poking out the 300 or so amps an average engine needs to turn it over at a reasonable cranking speed plus supplying enough to fire up the ignition.

The next thing to check is the tightness, cleanliness and condition of the battery terminals. There are four main types. The first, and one of the best, is the Ford type where you get a flat battery terminal with a hole in it and a flat connector on the end of the main leads. Provided they're clean and the cable is tightly attached to the connector, there's little to go wrong.

Most other batteries have round tapered terminal posts which can be a source of trouble depending on what type of connector you've got on the cables. The worst is the hood made from lead with a screw through the top of it. I long ago lost count of the number of starting problems I've found because of them. The hood's all right when it's new, but it soon gets out of shape and doesn't fit tightly on the post. This sets up a resistance which corrodes the inside of the hood which makes matters worse. Someone scrapes the inside, and this makes the fit even worse. Except for a couple to keep in museums to show how crude a terminal you can get, the lot ought to be chucked in the waste bin. Far superior are the clamp-on type known as SMMT connectors. Even here, you've got to keep an eye on them. If someone's let green or white corrosive crystals grow on the battery posts they eat away at the inside of the terminals and stop you getting a good connection.

The third type, which again work well

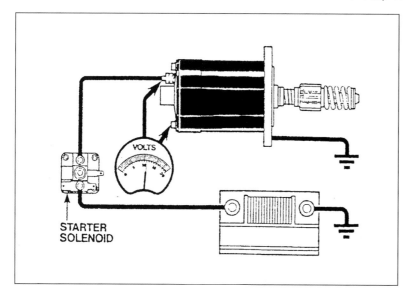

when they're new and clean but which deteriorate rapidly with corrosion are the ones found on Renaults and a couple of other French cars. They have a clamping piece, a thimble with a threaded stud on it and a plastic hand nut to tighten the whole lot together. If the thimbles and clamps get corroded, you can buy new ones at any Renault dealer.

Whatever type of terminal you've got, make sure it's clean and smear Vaseline over it to stop future corrosion.

Right, we've got a good battery, fully charged and with clean, bright and tight terminals. It ought to give out plenty of poke, so our next job is to find out why that poke isn't spinning the engine over.

Unless you've got an insulated return system, which is highly unlikely unless you're building a petrol tanker, the circuit completes its return through the chassis, or though earth as it's usually called. It can't complete its return if the earth lead from the battery isn't making good contact with the chassis. And I mean good, clean, metal to metal contact, not hit or miss contact through rust or coats of Hammerite. Make sure the terminal's clean, the part of the chassis it bolts to is clean and the connection is tight. Test with your meter set on ohms between the terminal spade to a clean part of the chassis. You should get zero ohms resistance, absolutely perfect contact.

The second part of the return circuit which many people overlook is the connection between the engine and the chassis. The engine sits on rubber mounts, which won't conduct a thing, so you've got to have an earthing strap or the starter current tries to complete the circuit through some piddling little contact like the choke cable. Usually, the earthing strap runs from one of the bell housing bolts to the chassis, and it should be a heavy cable at least the same as the main battery cables. Like the earthing strap from the battery, the terminals on the engine earthing strap must be clean and bright and in good metal to metal contact.

At least we're now in a position to give the battery a chance to do its stuff, so I'll move on to checking the main heavy-current starter circuit. Before I do, I'm going to give you a warning and I'm going to say it only once, so listen carefully.

A fully charged battery packs a lot of punch and if you're careless with cables or metal tools lying around the terminals anywhere in the main starter circuit you can get an

almighty flash over to earth. If the piece of metal happens to be a watch strap or a signet or wedding ring it will get very hot indeed and burn you badly. Take your watch off and, if you can't take the ring off, cover it with a piece of sticking plaster. I once worked with a chap who ignored this warning, shorted out the main cable with his signet ring and was off work for a week with a badly burned hand.

The second thing is that your meter isn't designed to take the full 300 or so amps starter current a battery can give, so don't do anything silly like trying to measure it. All you'll do is burn the inside of your meter to pieces.

OK. Remembering those safety precautions, I'll press on. There are five checks to make, and you'll need someone to sit in the car and turn the key.

Test One - check the battery terminal voltage under load
Test Two - check the starter terminal voltage under load
Test Three - check the voltage drop on the heavy main cables
Test Four - check the voltage drop across the solenoid
Test Five - check the voltage drop on the earth return

The first one is to check the battery terminal voltage under load. First check the voltage across the battery

Test 4. Keep cranking and look for a voltage drop across the solenoid terminals. If you get a high reading, suspect the solenoid. This is a separate solenoid for an inertia starter.

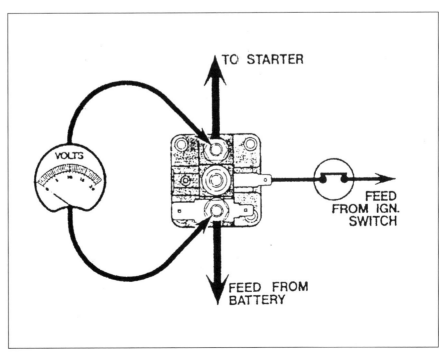

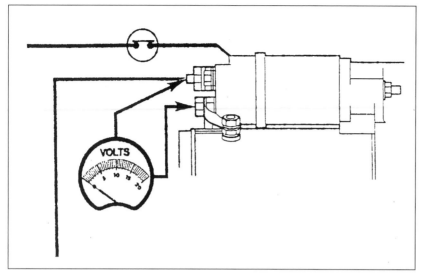

This is the same as test 4 but on a pre-engaged starter where the solenoid sits on the top.

terminals with nothing switched on. It should be 12 volts or slightly above. Disconnect the lead from the coil to the distributor, or take the rotor arm out, so the engine can't start, and get your helper to turn the key while you watch the voltage reading across the battery. You'll get a drop, but it should still be at least 9 to 9.5 volts. If the voltage drops right down, the starter's probably faulty, but we'll continue with our checks to make certain.

Test two is to check the starter terminal voltage under load. With your meter set to volts, check the voltage

The last of our five main checks is the voltage drop on the earth return. It should be zero. If it isn't, the starter may be faulty but first check for bad connections at the engine earthing strap or the battery earth lead.

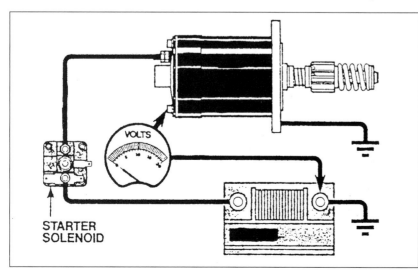

STARTER
SOLENOID

between the main starter terminal and the body of the starter when your helper switches the key to 'Start'. With a pre-engaged starter where the solenoid sits on top of the starter body, make sure you're checking the main starter terminal and not the solenoid terminal. You should get a reading within half a volt or so of the one you got in test one. If you get a lower reading there's a high resistance somewhere along the line either at one of the cable connectors or at the solenoid's internal contacts. The next three tests will tell you where.

On now to test three which checks the voltage drop on the heavy main cables. With the setting still on volts, connect your meter between the live battery terminal and the main terminal on the starter without turning the key to 'Start'. You should get battery voltage. When you turn the key to 'Start', the voltage should drop to practically zero. If you get a higher reading, check the cable or strap from the solenoid to the starter and the connections at the solenoid. Once again, they must be clean, bright and tight. If that doesn't find the trouble, move on to test four.

Check four tests the voltage drop across the solenoid. Without switching on, connect the meter across the two main solenoid terminals. You should get battery voltage and, like test three, this should drop to practically zero when the key is turned to 'Start'. If it doesn't, the betting is that the contacts inside the solenoid are giving trouble.

The last check is test five which checks the voltage drop on the earth return and re-checks your work on the earthing side of the battery and the engine earthing strap. This time, connect the meter between the battery earth terminal and the body of the starter motor. The voltage should be zero and should stay practically at zero when the key is turned to 'Start'. If it rises appreciably, go back and check the earth connections of the battery earth strap and the engine earthing strap.

These five checks shouldn't take more than ten minutes, and you've taken all the guesswork out of checking the starter and the starting circuit for faults. If it's the first time you've used a meter for systematic checking you'll realise how useful a tool it is and you'll find yourself using it more and more. With the diagrams, I've used a mixture of inertia and pre-engaged starters. The principles are the same whichever type you've got.

Part Two
PRE-ENGAGED STARTERS

The starter didn't want to know, you've been through the checks with a meter and decided, with a sinking feeling, that the starter needs replacing. Hang on a bit. Before you part with anything up to £100, spare half an hour or so to unbutton the old motor and see if it can be persuaded to accept another lease on life. In some cases, it can't, and an exchange is the only answer. But in at least half the cases of starter motors that are handed in for exchange, the owner could have got an extra year or more useful life for the cost of four carbon brushes, a couple of spire nuts and a bit of glasspaper.

Worth thinking about, eh? And the best part is that you've got nothing to lose except half an hour's time. If, when you strip it down you find burnt out segments on the commutator or field coils that are charred and horrible, you've only got to button it all up again and you're back to square one.

Most starters these days are the pre-engaged type with the solenoid sitting on top of the motor body. As the name suggests, the solenoid pushes the pinion into engagement with the flywheel ring gear before it turns the power on, which is much kinder on the pinion and the ring gear than the older type of inertia starter where the pinion whanged into the ring gear at high speed and full power.

Yes, pre-engaged starters are a little bit more complicated than the inertia type, but there's nothing black-artish about them. Once you get the hang of how they work they're quite simple. When you turn the key, the solenoid pushes on a lever which in turn pushes the pinion along its shaft to engage in the flywheel. Then it moves a bit further against a spring to turn on the power. There's a one-way clutch on the pinion drive so that if you hang on to the key too long the accelerating engine doesn't rip the guts out of the starter motor, and that's about it.

In most cases pre-engaged starters can be given a new lease of life with a clean, a new set of brushes and, possibly but not often, a change of solenoid. You can check the solenoid before you even start to go inside the motor.

Clamp your starter in the vice with a pair of soft jaws to stop damaging it and put your battery on the bench next to the starter. Then connect the earth terminal of the battery to one of the starter fixing holes. Use a heavy cable, the battery's normal earthing strap is ideal. Now take a cable from the positive side of the battery and touch it on the small push-on connector on top of the solenoid. When you do this, the solenoid should work and the pinion should be pushed forwards. Remove your positive lead and connect another positive lead, this time with heavy cable, from the battery to the big screw terminal on the solenoid that takes the main

After taking out the screws which hold the end cap you may have to prise off a spire nut.

Start your stripping by taking out the solenoid.

feed from the battery. The starter won't turn yet - or it shouldn't - because the solenoid hasn't yet completed the contact. Hold the starter firmly to stop it kicking, and run another positive lead to the small solenoid terminal just as before. This time, the solenoid should push the pinion forwards and, at the end of its travel, make contact across the main terminals so the starter spins. It will spin with quite a jump and plenty of

Take the large aluminium end cap off the drive end, and everything lifts out.

torque, which is why you want it clamped in the vice or, at very least, held to the bench by a big G-cramp.

The fact that the starter spins when it isn't under load doesn't necessarily mean it's OK. When it tries to turn the engine it may well fail, or be very sluggish, because of worn brushes and a dirty commutator.

Take off the short electric link cable which joins the starter and the solenoid. Then start your stripping by undoing the two bolts which hold the solenoid and unhooking it from the end of the lever. Sometimes there's a large rubber boot over the end of the solenoid plunger so you can't see what you're doing, but all you have to do once the nuts are off is to push the solenoid in slightly against a spring, lift it up, and out it comes. Watch out that you don't lose the anti-vibration packing piece under the solenoid. Put the solenoid safely to one side so you don't get it covered in muck, and turn you attention to the end plate furthest from the drive.

Here, you might come across several ways of holding the end plate and the end of the armature. Holding the plate you might find two long bolts or four small bolts, and holding the end of the armature you might find a collar with a split pin or one of those horribly cheap but very efficient hammer-on spire nuts. If you've got a spire nut, the only way to get it off is to be brutal and lever it off with a big screwdriver. It won't want to shift at first, but go round and round it levering a bit at a time, and eventually it will fly off and disappear over the other side of the garage. Don't bother to chase it, spire nuts are cheap enough, and it's not safe to use them twice. They spring the wrong way and don't hold properly.

When you levered it off, the sharp bits on the spire nut will have raised pips and grooves in the end of the armature shaft, and if you try to lift the end plate off the pips will stick in the end bearing and ruin it. Don't force things, go round with a fine file smoothing the pips off so that the end plate lifts off easily.

Almost all pre-engaged starters have got end-face commutators, and the brushes sit in a plastic holder which is riveted to the end plate. Two of the brushes will lift out with the plate because they're fixed to the terminal post, and two will stay behind because their leads are spot welded to the field coils. When you buy new brushes you might just get four separate brushes with leads on them, but if you buy a genuine maker's set you'll probably get two fixed to a new terminal post and two separate ones.

You can't solder the leads of the new brushes directly on to the field coil terminal because it's usually made of aluminium, so what you have to do is cut the old leads about an inch or so from the terminal, and solder the leads of your new brushes to the ends. The leads are made of copper so, provided they're clean, soldering should be a doddle. Remember to push an extra bit of insulating sleeve on the leads before you solder them so you can feed this down over the joint. If you bought a 'pattern' set of brushes that didn't come with a terminal post, do the same with the other two. I know the terminal post's made of brass, but it's easier to solder a couple of pairs leads together than solder two leads to a thick piece of brass.

However, I'm jumping ahead of myself a bit. Before you start soldering new brushes in, go to the other end of the starter and take out the pin on which the armature lever pivots. Again, you might come across one of two types. The most common is a plain pin held by another spire nut, so you deal with this the same way as you did with the bigger one on the armature shaft. On heavier duty starters you might find that the pin is eccentric, and is locked by a nut. With this type, you have to turn the eccentric to get the right pinion clearance, but I'll come to that in a few minutes.

Once you've got the lever pin out, you can undo the two screws that hold the big aluminium cover over the pinion, and lift it off. Now you can lift the armature out of the starter body, or yoke as starter makers call it, and start inspecting the parts. The commutator ought to be flat and clean. It probably won't be, but if it's only dirty you can clean it up with a drop or two of petrol on a rag. If it's dirty, or got a few not very deep grooves in it, wrap a piece of glasspaper over a flat piece of wood and polish them out. Make sure you rub the face of the commutator down evenly, and not all on one side, or the brushes will have to bob in and out like mad things and won't be very inclined to keep good contact.

If, however, the segments of the commutator are burnt a deep pitted black, or worn down like the surface of an un-made road, screw it all together again and resign yourself to buying an exchange motor. Well, at least you tried.

Now have a look inside the body, or yoke. It'll be full of muck and copper dust, so give it a good dust out with a brush, or an airline if you're lucky enough to have a compressor. Take a good look at the insulation of the field coils. Apart from being a bit dirty, it should be in good condition, but if it's charred anywhere the coils have been shorting out, and the starter's had it.

Two of the brushes are fixed to the field coils, and the other two are fixed to the terminal post in the end cap.

Don't try taking the field coils out, whatever you might read in ancient repair books. They're held temptingly by a couple of large screws, but these screws are put in really tight by a machine with a big wheel on the top to turn the screwdriver bit, and the coils are held centrally and tight against the body by an expander before the screws are done up. Even if you manage to get the screws undone by brute force and an impact driver, you'll never get them centred again.

As well as looking at the coil insulation, check what looks like a piece of thick grey paper behind the coil terminal where the brushes are welded on. It isn't grey paper, it's a special insulating material. If it's burnt, the terminal strip has been arcing to the starter body. You might be lucky and get away with packing a new piece of insulation behind the terminal, but don't bank on it. Do that only if you absolutely must in order to get you out of hole (like not having any more money). You might get away with it, but it's a temporary repair at best.

The last thing to look at is the pinion drive and clutch. With a pre-engaged starter you'll be very unlucky to find any wear on these, because they're designed not to wear out, but nothing's infallible. Slightly more likely, but not all that likely, is a sticking clutch or a clutch that doesn't clutch at all. Hold the body of the clutch and try turning the pinion back and forth. It should turn easily one way, and lock up immediately you try to turn it the other way. If it doesn't turn freely one way, the engine will drive the starter at very high speed when it fires, and that's why you found the insides burnt out. If it doesn't hold tight immediately you turn the pinion the other way, or grips and slips, the starter will never turn the engine over properly.

You can't buy new clutch assemblies very easily unless you go to a starter reconditioning firm, and they'll probably want to sell you an exchange starter anyway. But if you're cannibalising a few old starters to make one good one you can take the clutch assembly off after you lever off a snap ring on the armature shaft. Sometimes you can get at the snap ring easily, but on some heavy duty motors you have to knock back a fairly tight collar first. A long socket's ideal for doing this.

Both end plates have bronze bushes, and when the makers recondition them as-new, they always put new bushes in. Try them just to make sure, but the chances are you'll find very little wear. After all, starters don't turn over all that much. Compared with the rest of the machinery they do sudden short bursts of heavy work at infrequent intervals.

Let's be optimistic, and hope that all you've got to do is give the parts a clean, clean up the face of the commutator and fit new brushes. In well over half the cases of reluctant, tired pre-engaged starters you'll find that this will rejuvenate them wonderfully.

Start your reassembly by putting the armature in the body and bolting on the aluminium end plate at the drive end. Now put the brushes in their holders, put the end plate on and screw that in position. Now you've got to set the armature end float. It must have some end float or it won't work properly, but the amount isn't all that critical. About 30 to 40 thou will be about right.

If the armature was held in the brush end cap by a collar and a split pin you can adjust the end float with shim washers. It's a bit more tricky when you've got to hammer a spire nut on. There's a plain washer under the spire nut, and the easiest way is to put an old feeler gauge under this plain washer while you tap the spire nut down with a piece of tube.

Stand the starter upright so the other end of the armature is sitting on something solid or you'll push the bush out of the drive end plate. Go easy with tapping on the tube, because if you get the spire nut too tight,

This commutator will clean up with glasspaper, but if it's burnt, it's had it.

it's a real pain trying to lever it up again.

There's a way to guard against this, but you won't find it in any of the books, certainly not in the maker's training manual, because it isn't quite pukka engineering practice. Before you put the aluminium end cap on the drive end, have a look at the bronze bush, and if it isn't sticking through the inside, tap it in slightly so it's about a sixteenth of an inch or so proud of the aluminium.

Now if you're unlucky enough to get the spire nut too tight, make sure no-one's looking, and do a bit of fiddle-bodging by using a small punch to tap the bronze bush at the drive end out just a few thou. Be careful not to burr it so the shaft gets tight. And don't tell anyone I told you to do it!

Once you've got the armature back in, fit the pin through the lever that the solenoid pushes, and if it's a plain one you can tap the spire nut on and leave it at that. If it's an eccentric pin you have to set the pinion clearance, and this means energising the solenoid. If you've got a six volt supply, or if you've got a battery with exposed link bars so you can tap six volts off it with crocodile clips, use six volts. If you haven't, and you've got to use 12 volts, don't keep the solenoid energised for more than 10 seconds or so at a time or you might

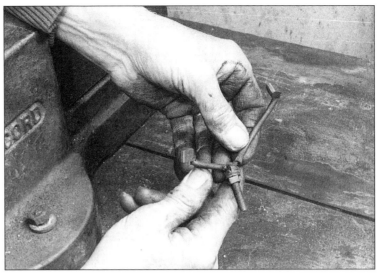

You may get two of the new brushes already fixed to a new terminal post.

well burn out the windings. If you don't get the setting right first time, disconnect and let things cool down.

When you energise the solenoid, the pinion will fly

Check the one-way clutch on the drive. It must lock instantly, and be free the other way.

forward, and you want a clearance of about 15 thou between the front face of the pinion and the thrust collar. Turn the eccentric pin till you get the right clearance, and lock it up.

Now all you have to do is put the solenoid anti-vibration pad in position, hook the end of the solenoid plunger over the top of the lever and button it all up.

Before you fit it back on the car, give it test by clamping the body of the starter in the vice and putting two jump leads from a battery to it, one to the main terminal of the solenoid and the other to the body of the starter motor. Now take a flying 12 volt lead and touch it on the small push-on terminal of the solenoid, the one that takes the lead from the starter relay. The solenoid should push the pinion in smartly, and the armature should whizz round. Keep the power on for only a second or so because starters don't like running without a load. They get all hot and bothered. Remember, don't try testing it without clamping it in a vice or under a big G-clamp. When the power comes on, there's a lot of torque reaction flying about, and it'll twist out of your hands on to the floor.

And that's it. Fit it back on the car and it should turn the engine over a treat. And you can congratulate yourself on saving a medium sized wad of the folding stuff.

Part Three
INERTIA STARTERS

If your donor car is a modern one, it will have a pre-engaged starter but, if it was an older one, it will probably have an inertia starter. Just in case you're not

You'll find two types of inertia starter. The top one has a face commutator and no access band on the outside. The lower type has an axial commutator with an access band for the brushes.

clear about the difference, on a pre-engaged starter, which I looked at in part 2, the pinion moves gently into engagement with the ring gear on the flywheel before the motor begins to turn whereas, on an inertia starter, the motor turns first and then the pinion whangs into mesh with the stationary ring gear.

As you'll appreciate, the pinion has quite a hard life, not to mention the shock load on the starter motor, and it's tribute to them that they last as long as they do. There comes a time, however, when they've had enough. In some cases, the starter's beyond economic salvage but, with a surprisingly high proportion, a few pounds spent on new brushes plus a couple of hours easy work will see it fit for several years' more service. It's a lot cheaper then shelling out for a replacement.

When you've got the starter off, move the pinion back and forth along the shaft. It should move freely and easily. If it feels sticky, gritty or notchy, it won't be reliable and it needs taking to pieces to overhaul it. This is about the only time you're likely to run into a snag because, unless it's a very early starter, you need a special tool to compress the large spring on the shaft. On early inertia starters, the pinion was held on the shaft by a castellated collar with a left-hand thread, and locked with a split pin. With these, life is easy, you just take out the pin and unscrew the ring. On later models, which you've probably got, the collar is held by a circlip and you have to compress the spring to take the circlip off.

The compressor is quite a simple affair and you used to be able to buy them for a pound or two in most accessory shops but I enquired at three shops in my area and they no longer keep them.

You might be lucky and find that your local shop still has a compressor in stock but, if not, it isn't difficult to make one. As you can see from the picture, all it consists of is a couple of large, thick washers with one of them cut to look like a horseshoe, and a couple of bolts to pull them together. The one I have has one of the washers threaded to take the bolts but bolts and nuts would serve just as well. The tools were made before we all went metric and only slightly critical dimension is the size of the holes which, measuring mine, should be one inch diameter (25.4mm if you're working in metric).

The slot which forms the horseshoe is an inch wide and the washers are a quarter of an inch (6.35mm) thick. Don't go any thinner because the spring's quite strong. The bolts or, correctly, setscrews as they are threaded all the way up, are a quarter-inch BSF, but slightly larger ones would do. The outside of the washers is 2 3/8 inch diameter

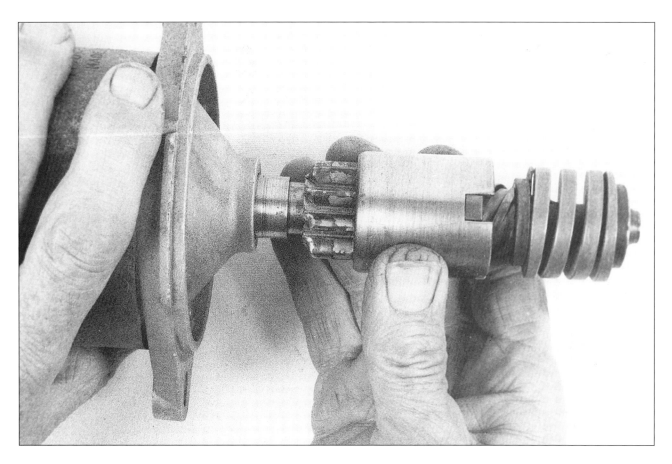

but this isn't important and a square or rectangular plate would suit just as well.

To use the tool, you wind the pinion down the shaft a little, slip the tool on and tighten the bolts to compress the spring clear of the retaining collar. The collar usually sticks, so tap it down to expose the wire circlip which you can prise off with a screwdriver. Then the retaining collar, spring, helix collar and pinion all slide off the shaft.

If the pinion sticks, it's usually because of old oil and dirt and, if it's notchy, it's usually because of burrs on the splines of the shaft. Wash everything off in white spirit and try the helix collar along the shaft. If it doesn't slide freely you might have to dress the burrs on the shaft splines with a fine file but, apart from that, the drives are usually in quite good condition. If the teeth on the pinion are badly worn your best bet is to find a secondhand starter with a pinion in better shape and make one good one out of the two. The same pinions were used on quite a few different makes of car.

Moving now to the other end of the starter, the commutator and brush gear, you might have one of two types, the older type with an axial commutator has a metal band clamped round the outside which you take off to get at the brushes. The later type has a face commutator with no band round the outside.

Dealing first with the older type, make a hook from a

On either type, check the drive first. The pinion should be free to turn and return with no sticking or roughness.

piece of fairly stout wire, lift the circular brush springs, pull the brushes halfway out and wedge them there by putting the springs against their sides. Now you can

If you need to strip the pinion for cleaning, you need this tool. If you can't buy one it isn't difficult to make.

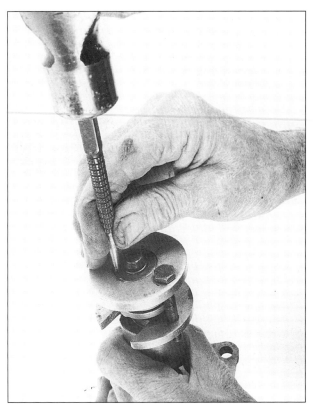

undo the long through-bolts which hold the starter together and pull the armature and commutator out from the drive end. Lift the brushes right out, drop the ends of the brush springs in the top of the metal brush holders to save them uncoiling, take the nuts, washers and spacers off the main terminal post and pull the end cover off. Two of the brushes will come with it and two will stay behind attached to the field coils.

The inside of the starter body will be covered in copper dust as the brushes are made from sintered copper with a small amount of carbon. Dust it all out because it's a conductor and can cause shorts. If the insulation of the field coils, or the terminal post, are in a bad way you might be better off looking for starter in better condition but if, as is likely, they dust off OK, you're left with the commutator and the brushes. Clean the commutator with fine glasspaper - don't use emery paper or wet and dry as these contain carborundum which can short out the commutator segments. Unless it's badly ridged it will clean up well. Badly ridged ones

You use the tool to compress the large spring at the end of the pinion drive. With the spring compressed you can free the coned collar that holds it. It may be tight, so tap it down with a punch.

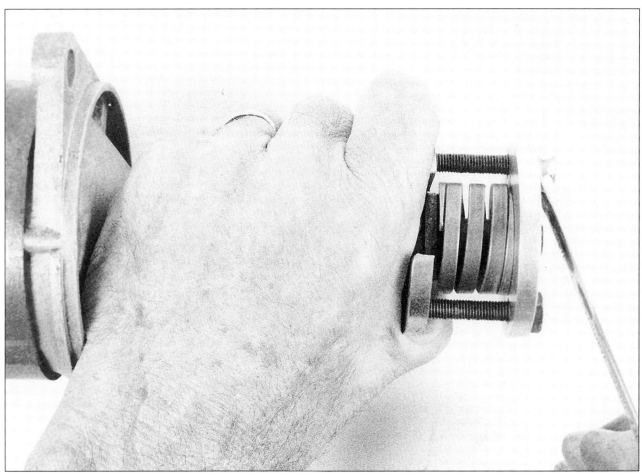

can be skimmed in a lathe but this is fairly expensive so, once again, look for another starter. Don't undercut the insulation between the segments on a starter's commutator. You do this only on dynamos.

If the brushes are worn down so that the circular spring hits, or almost hits, the metal brush holder before it puts pressure on the brush, you need knew brushes. You can get them in accessory shops or from auto electrical dealers but you can't solder them directly to the starter as the old ones are spot welded. What you do is cut the old brush cable about an inch or so from the brush, cut the cable on the new ones and solder the two cables together. Remember to slip a length of insulated sleeving on the field coil brush cables before you solder them. Check that the new brushes are free in their housings and, if not, ease them

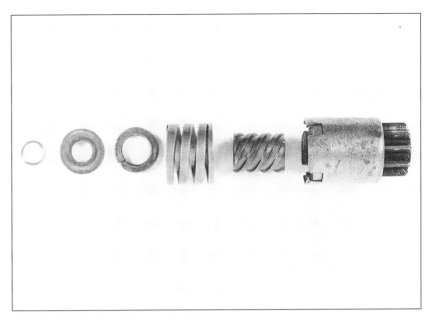

With the collar and circlip off, the drive just pulls off the end of the starter shaft.

with a fine file. Older books and manuals tell you to bed the new brushes in to the commutator using a piece of glasspaper but it's a fiddling business and not very easy to do. I've always left the ends of the brushes flat and found that they soon bed in of their own accord.

Putting things back is much the same as taking them apart. The armature will go in easily if you wedge the brushes halfway out of their holders as you did when you took things apart. Lucas says that the pinion and it's drive should be sparingly lubricated with a special grease but I've found that any grease tends to attract dirt which makes the pinion sticky. I always assemble them dry and clean and haven't found any adverse effects.

On the later type of motor with the face armature, the pinion drive is the same and attention to the commutator and brushes is similar but much simpler. Here, you have a brush end plate held by four small hexagon headed screws. When you undo them the plate lifts off complete with two brushes, this time with the terminal post, and two stay behind, just like the older type. The brushes are triangular and run in housings in a plastic moulding on the end cap. Pressure to push them against the commutator is provided by coil springs in the plastic moulding. Check that the coil springs have spring left in them and that the brushes are free in the housings. Once again, if your new brushes are too tight, ease them off with a fine file. The armature comes out after you undo two screws at the other end and, as before, get rid of all the dust inside before you button it all together again.

Once the collar is free you can take off the circlip that holds it on.

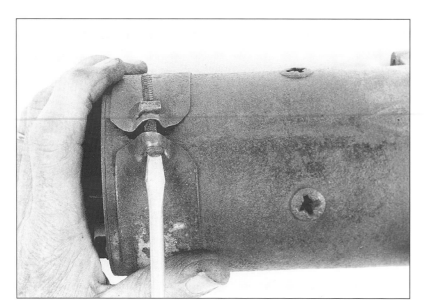

The next step on axial commutator motors is to undo the band over the brushes.

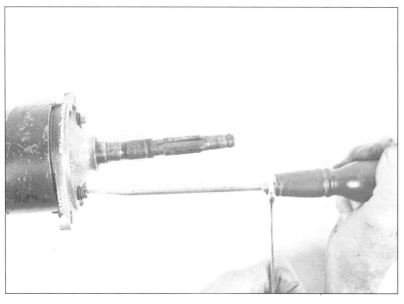

Now you can undo the long through-bolts that hold the body together. They may be tight, so choose a screwdriver on which you can use spanner assistance.

Make yourself a wire hook to hold the brush springs, and wedge the brushes halfway up in their holders clear of the commutator. Be careful when you lift the through-bolts out, as the starter will fall apart.

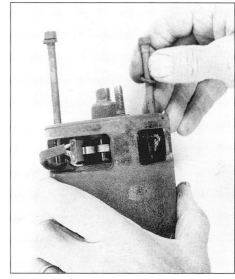

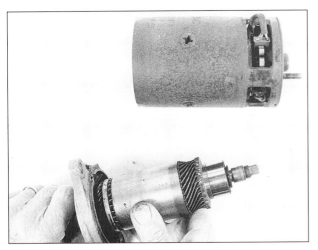

Above: Once the through-bolts are out, lift the armature out from the drive shaft end complete with the end plate.

Above right: Undo the main terminal nuts, lift the brushes up and hook the springs in the brush holders to stop them uncoiling before you lift the brush plate off.

Right: The brush leads are spot welded in the body so, if you have to renew them, cut the leads and solder the new ones to the cut ends.

On the face commutator starter, after the pinion is off, begin stripping by undoing the main terminal nuts.

Keep the terminal nuts and insulating washers in order so you know where to put them back.

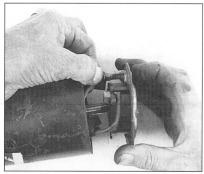

Left: The brush plate is held by four quite small bolts. Above: When these bolts are undone you can lift the brush plate clear. Two brushes will lift out with it and two will stay in the body.

Left: With the brush plate off, the armature pulls out from the brush end of the body. Above: The brushes are wedge shaped and fit in recesses in the plastic part of the end cap.

Below: Check the brush springs which are inside the recesses in the end cap. They must be free to keep the brushes against the commutator. Right: If the commutator is dirty, clean it with fine glasspaper. Don't loose the shim washer which governs the end float.

Chapter 10

CHARGE OF THE LIGHTING BRIGADE

Overhauling an alternator could save you a packet. So, have a look inside before forking out for an exchange unit.

SOME MANUALS TELL YOU THAT ALTERNATORS DON'T need servicing, and leave it at that. Others tend to skirt round the subject and tell you to take the car to your local dealer for a check without telling you that he'll be pleased to relieve you of anything from £80 to £150 for an exchange unit when the chances are that yours can be put right for anything between a fiver and twenty quid.

Part One
LUCAS ACR SERIES

There are quite a few makes of alternator, but one of the most popular ones from a donor car is the Lucas ACR range which don't need an external regulator. You might still find a donor car from the early days of alternators fitted with the Lucas AC range, usually a 10AC or 11AC, which did use an external regulator, but these are more difficult to service and not so efficient as the ACRs, and parts are becoming more difficult to find, so you'd be better off swapping to an ACR which you can get from any breakers quite easily.

Make sure you get the later 'machine sensing' model, as the early ACR battery-sensing models weren't so reliable. You can spot the difference straight away because the

This is the plate which identifies a Lucas ACR alternator.

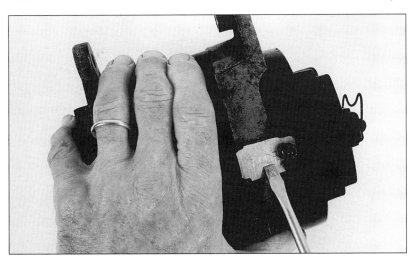

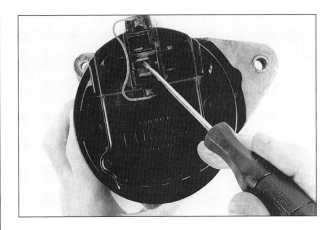

Quite a few alternator troubles are caused by corrosion of the main terminal connectors. Check the terminals on the end of the cable as well as in the alternator.

machine-sensing models have the so-called European termination, using only one connecting block with three push-on Lucar connectors in it.

Unless the front bearing's worn, because someone's mounted the alternator out of line with the other pulleys, or strained the fan belt far too tight, you can overhaul it without having to take the pulley off or take out the long through-bolts that hold the main body parts together.

Start by taking off the black plastic cover which is held by two 1/4 inch AF bolts. They're shrouded quite deep in the cover, so you'll need a small socket or box spanner. Under this you'll find the diode rectifier pack on to which the connector plugs, a fairly large white nylon brush housing and, attached to this, a square aluminium box which is the regulator.

On ACR alternators built before 1980 or thereabouts you might also find a separate diode, looking a bit like a small capacitor out of a distributor. It sits alongside the rectifier unit, on its right when you're holding the alternator with the connectors at the top. This is the surge protection diode, put there to protect the regulator if someone's silly

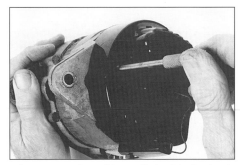

Above: Start by taking off the black plastic end cover. The bolts are shrouded so you'll need either a small socket and extension or, as we've used here, a nut spinner.
Right: Clean the main terminals to get them free of rust and muck. This is where one of your small files comes in useful.

Above left: Before you can get to the brushes you have to undo the regulator and its wiring. It's held by one screw at the top and two small arms atthe bottom. Above right: With the regulator out of the way you can undo the small bolts which hold down the brush retaining plates. Below: Lift the brushes out and check their length. Lucas says renew them if they're worn down less than 5/16 inch long. If they're sticky in their holders, clean them with fine glasspaper.

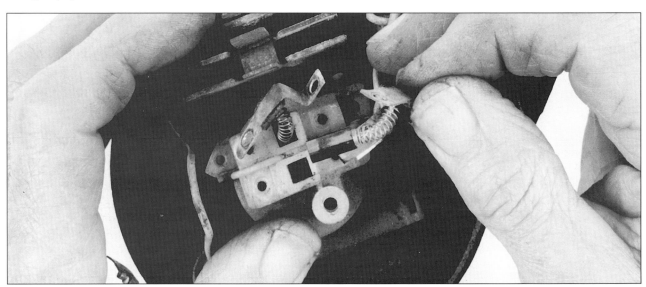

Now you can get at the two bolts which hold the white nylon cover over the slip ring. Left: When you lift the cover off you may find, as here, that the face of the slip ring is badly tarnished.

leave it on as extra protection.

All ACR alternators built for the past 15 or so years are fitted with the improved 14TR type regulator, and when Lucas first introduced it they either painted it gold or put a gold band on it to indicate that it didn't need a surge protection diode. However, as the older models got fewer and fewer in Lucas service centres, they couldn't be bothered with the gold paint and went back to a plain aluminium box. The only way to tell if a plain aluminium 14TR is an improved model or not is by the part number, but your local Lucas service centre ought not to have any difficulty identifying your old one, and if you buy a new regulator it will be the improved type.

If you're thinking of cannibalising another alternator for a regulator, watch the colour of the leads and try to check the wiring diagram of the car from which it came. Some ACR regulators were made for temperature sensing, and the main lead to the starter solenoid went via a heat sensor mounted as close to the battery as possible. This lowered the voltage when the battery was hot and raised it when the battery was cold. The connecting wires on a normal machine sensing regulator are coloured black, yellow, red and white. On a temperature sensing regulator the white is replaced by an orange lead.

enough remove a battery terminal with the engine running.

A short-circuited surge protection diode is quite likely the culprit if the ignition warning light stays on when you rev up the engine and you've checked the obvious things like dirty connections and fan belt tension. A faulty regulator can also make the ignition warning light to stay on, and in this case the warning light sometimes gets brighter as you rev up. Later ACR alternators don't have a surge protection diode as the regulator was improved and didn't need it. If you fit one of the later regulators you can leave the surge protection diode off, though if it's in good order you can

You can check and change the brushes without taking anything else off. Each brush is attached to a small metal strip held to the top of the brush housing by two tiny hexagon-headed screws. However, it's easier, and better, to take the brush housing off so that you can clean the slip ring and also clean the inside of the brush housing which will probably be covered in carbon dust which can short things out.

The regulator is attached to the top of the brush housing, so you have to disconnect it first. Make a note of where the connections go. Before you start taking anything off, there's a simple, though not infallible, check you can carry out on the regulator. Take the alternator back over to the car, plug it in and switch the ignition on. Earth the body of the alternator, and then earth the regulator box body to the alternator body. With the regulator body earthed, the ignition warning light should not come on. If it does, the regulator is possibly faulty.

Lucas says that if the brushes are less than 5/16 inch long they should be renewed. Unlike brushes on a dynamo, brushes on an ACR alternator don't have to be bedded in as they run on a flat slip ring and not on a curved commutator. The outer brush wears quicker than the central one, but for some reason the central brush seems to wear the slip ring faster. On a well-worn alternator you sometimes find it's almost drilled a hole the centre connector on the slip ring.

If the slip ring is in good condition apart from being glazed you can clean it up with fine sandpaper, not emery as this leaves carborundum dust embedded in it. If it's worn, it needs renewing, but we'll come to that in a moment.

If someone (not you, of course!) tried to connect the battery the wrong way round, or put jump leads on the wrong way round, or even did some electric welding on the body without disconnecting the alternator first, there's a chance that they've blown the diodes in the rectifier. A poor connection between the brushes and the slip ring, particularly intermittent connection, can also blow diodes. A warning of this is an ignition warning light that flickers on and off when you rev up. If this happens to you, check the brushes and the slip ring as soon as possible.

And that's as far as it's practical to go on home overhauling an ACR alternator, and it will cure many cases of low output or even no output at all. It's possible to replace the diode pack if some of them have blown, and it's possible to replace the front bearing, but in these cases, we'd say you're better off looking for an alternator without these faults, or trading it in against a reconditioned one.

If you've got a lot of electrical equipment on the car you can change up from a 15ACR or 16ACR to a 17ACR, outputs of the 15, 16 and 17 being 28, 34 and 36 amps. Most popular for smaller cars is the 17ACR because it has a low cutting-in speed of 950 rpm compared with the 1,000 or 1,250 rpm of the others, and will poke out a good charge on a fastish tick-over, quite an advantage in stop-go traffic when you've got a lot of electrics on.

If you need even more output you can swap to one of

Above: If the slip ring's just tarnished but not damaged, clean it up with fine glasspaper. Don't use emery or wet and dry paper as these contain carburundum which is a conductor, and the dust will short things out. Below: Before you put the alternator on the car, check that this small bush is free to move in the body casing. It's job is to take up any differences of dimension in the stamped out holding bracket but, if it's seized, you might break the alternator body when you try to tighten the bolts.

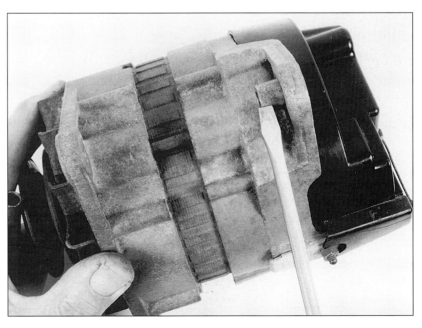

the current range of Lucas A-series alternators which you find on cars like Sierras, Granadas and even some of the later Escorts with big electrical demands. In most cases, the ACR bracketry will suit but, if not, you may have to get the bracket with the alternator. The wiring should be the same, though it's as well to check the diagram just to make certain.

If your donor car used a Bosch alternator the principles of overhaul are very similar to the Lucas one and you can also swap Bosch alternators about to get a higher output one. With all swapping, watch the fan belt size. Sometimes you find that the fan belt either won't go on, or won't tension tight enough because you've come to the end of the adjustment, so you might find that you need a slightly different size of fan belt. In that case it's a matter of shopping around. Make sure that the cross section of the vee on the alternator pulley is the same as the one on the crankshaft, and pick a belt that fits snugly without bottoming in the groove. It should run on the sloping vee sides so it gets a good grip.

Part Two
LUCAS A-SERIES

Overhauling the larger Lucas range of A-series alternators is very similar to overhauling the ACR range, but there are a few differences so we'll run through those to make sure you don't get the two types muddled up.

When you take the end cover off you'll see that the biggest difference is in the layout of the diodes. On the A-series alternators they don't sit in a vertical pack, they're on a half-moon plate.

It says 'Ford' on the end cover of this alternator, but it isn't made by Ford, they buy in all their electrics.

You don't need to touch the diodes to check and clean the brushes and slip rings, nor to renew the regulator and, as there's quite a lot of delicate soldering involved in removing them, we'd advise leaving the diode pack severely alone.

The regulator leads either unclip or unbolt from their terminals and, after taking out its fixing bolt, you can lift the regulator up and out of the way. Some of the regulator bolts also hold the brush plates and the brushes sit in the side of the slip ring housing because, unlike the ACR alternators where the slip ring is end-faced, the slip ring on an A-series alternator is in line with the armature, more like a commutator on an electric motor.

The slip ring cover on an A-series is held by two small bolts, and you need a socket and an extension to reach them. In our pictures we've taken the diode pack out,

Above: Its true identity is revealed on a plate at the side where, as you can see, it is a Lucas A133-55, an A-series alternator with a 55-amp output. Below: The first test on a second hand alternator is to give the pulley a good spin. If it feels gritty, or the bearings screech, forget it.

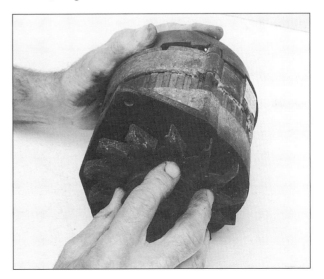

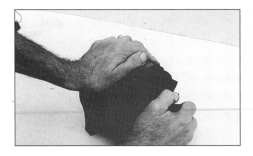

Above: After spinning it, grip the pulley really hard and try to rock it. If you feel even the slightest rick, look for another one. Right: Before taking the end cover off you have to remove the radio suppressor. Don't forget to put it back or you'll be wondering why you get a hissing interference on your stereo.

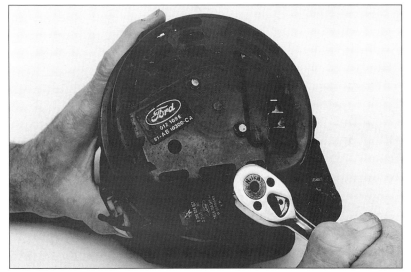

Left: This particular capacitor is a rectangular one, but some are tubular. Undo its fixing and lift it off. Below: As with the ACR range, the end cover is held by shrouded bolts.

The inside will probably be full of old carbon dust and muck, so give it a good brush out.

As with all alternators, half the troubles of low charge come from corrosion of the main terminals. Make sure they're clean and bright.

which makes access easier, because it was damaged. Once again, you'll probably find the slip rings coated with tarnish but, in most cases they will clean up with fine glasspaper.

As with the ACR range, we wouldn't advise going any further in overhaul although it's possible and I've run through the procedure for checking out and replacing a diode. However, if the slip ring's damaged, the diodes blown or the bearings are worn or seized, button it up and look for one in better condition.

Left: Next to corrosion in the no-charge stakes come worn brushes and dirty slip rings. The two brushes are under these plates. Start by undoing the top bolt first. Above: Then undo the small bolt on top of the brush housing, the one which takes the yellow lead from the regulator. You can see here how corrosion bites deep. The terminal plate for this bolt had corroded clean away from the diode block where I'm pointing the screwdriver.

Below: You can then undo the bottom bolt from the brush housing.
Right: Lift out the two brushes with their springs. The brushes normally sit on the ends of the springs, but they usually pop sideways when you pull them out.

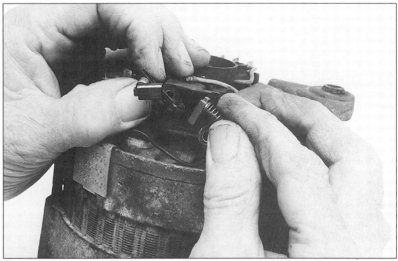

If you need a new regulator (symptoms being too high or too low a charge rate even when everything else is OK) there are two more leads to undo. One, the red one, fits on a terminal behind the main group of three.

The last regulator lead, the black one, goes to a small bolt on the bottom of the diode block, one of the bolts that holds the diode block in place.

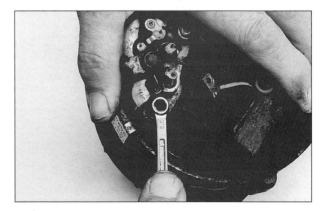

Above: Then you can undo the regulator fixing bolt and lift it off. Normally, the next stage would be to look at the slip rings, but I'll deal the with diodes first because it's easier to photograph the slip rings when the diodes are out of the way. Below: First step in taking the diodes off it to unsolder the three leads. Just in case they aren't blown, and as a precaution when you put the new block in, use a pair of pliers as a heat sink to stop the diodes getting too hot while you unsolder the leads. Remember which lead goes where, though it's usually plain enough.

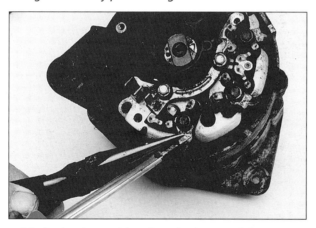

With the leads unsoldered, undo the remaining two screws holding the diode block. One is at the end.

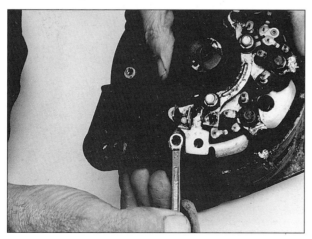

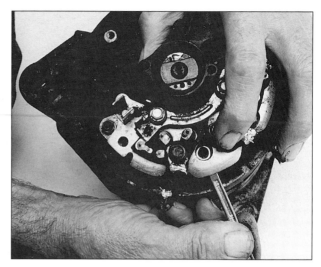

Above: The other screw is in the middle. There's a convenient hole above it so you can see now why I said a small socket set is a big help. It takes ages to undo this bolt with a spanner a sixth of a turn at a time. Below: Once the bolts are free you can lift the diode block away. I'll show you how to test the diodes in a moment but, first, I'll deal with the slip rings.

The plastic brush box is held on by two small bolts. If you're looking at the slip ring without taking off the diodes, a small socket is essential to get at these bolts.

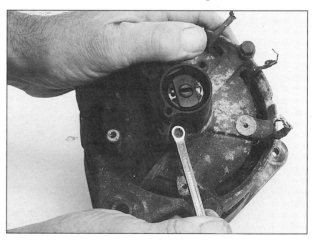

Above left: Lift the brush box off, and the slip ring is revealed in all its glory - well, usually it's black and grotty. Above right: If the slip ring is chewed and scored, button it all up and exchange the unit. But if, like this one, it's only dirty, a few moments work with fine glasspaper had the slip ring looking like new. Look at the difference between the first ring and second ring.

You probably won't have to test the diodes, or even take them off, but I'll show you how to do it, just in case. You can use a lamp and battery, but I've used a meter set on diode test. First, test the filed diodes. With the negative lead on the negative connector terminal at the group of three, touch the positive lead to the ends of each of the diodes marked A in the line drawing below. You should get continuity. If you don't, the diodes have blown. Now reverse the connections and try again. This time you should not get continuity. If you do, the diodes have gone short circuit.

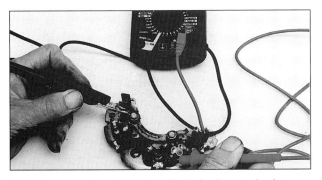

This line drawing shows the field diodes marked A, the positive diodes marked B and the negative diodes marked C. The points marked D and E are terminals.

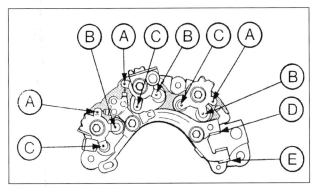

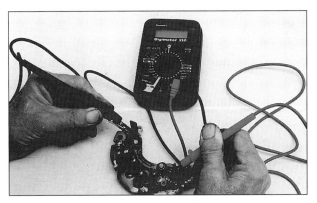

Above: Now the positive diodes. Move the negative lead of the meter, or the lamp and battery, to one of the large terminals of the group of three, and touch the positive lead to the ends of the diodes marked B in the line drawing. Again, you should get continuity. Reverse the connections and you should not get continuity. Below: Lastly, the negative diodes. Move the negative terminal of your meter to the base plate, the lower one, of the diode block and touch the positive terminal to the ends of the diodes marked C in the line drawing. This time you should not get continuity. Reverse the connections, and you should get continuity.

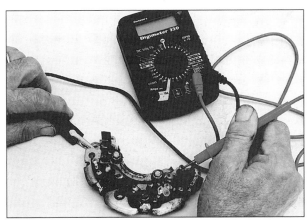

The innards of a Lucas A133-55. Sometimes you'll find a surge protection diode (arrowed) under the plastic cover, but it isn't fitted on all alternators. Test it the same way as the other diodes. It should pass current one way, but not the other.

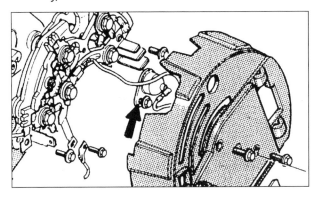

Chapter 11

ELECTRIC PUMPING STATION

Fed up with waiting for a mechanical fuel pump to fill the float chamber?

Fit an electric one.

IF YOU'VE CHOSEN A FORD WITH A CARBURETTOR engine, or some other makes, as your donor it will be fitted with a mechanical fuel pump driven off the engine, but you may want to change this for an electric pump because, though mechanical pumps are reliable enough, if the carb's run dry or the petrol in it has evaporated, you have wait with the engine cranking over before it fills the carb with enough petrol to start. There are two main types of electric pump used on kit cars, the SU and the Facet. I'll deal first with

This is what an SU pump looks like when it's completely dismantled.

overhauling the SU. They aren't difficult pumps to overhaul, but so many people make a muck of it because they don't know how to set them up. Follow the steps carefully and you shouldn't have any problems.

Over the years, SU electric fuel pumps have varied in details, mainly in the layout of the valves, and some are doubles (two horizontally opposed units working on a single central body to double the rate of flow) but despite these differences they all work on the same principle and they're all very similar to overhaul.

There's just one important point you have to watch. Some SU pumps are made to fit at the back of the car in

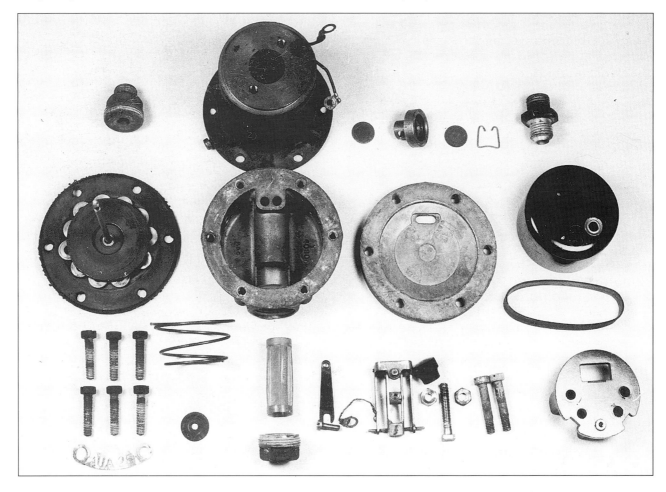

the boot and some are made to fit under the bonnet near the engine. They're commonly known as 'push' and 'pull' pumps. They'll often work wherever you put them but, for best results, if you've got a 'push' pump, fit it at the back and if it's a 'pull' pump, fit it at the front or you may find you get slight fuel starvation at high revs. The manual for the donor car will tell you where it was originally fitted.

Problems with an SU pump usually come from sticking or worn contact points, sticking valves, dirty filters, or, more rarely, a diaphragm which has gone hard and lost its flexibility. There are differences in settings for different cars, so for details you should consult the donor's manual or, if you're using a repair kit from SU, the leaflet which will cover all the types of pump for which the kit is suitable. In some cases, even though the particular model pump has been out of production for some time, Rover (or BLMC, BMC or whatever) are the biggest users of SUs and their dealers often have repair kits in stock for older model pumps. In any case, SU has always kept modern pumps in production which are direct replacements for older models, so you should never be entirely stuck.

If you're dealing with a secondhand pump from an autojumble or the breaker's yard there will most likely be a nasty stale-smelling deposit of old petrol varnish inside the body. In some old manuals and books on car repair you might read that the way to get rid of this is to boil the parts in caustic soda solution followed by a dip in strong nitric acid, and a good rinse in boiling water.

Forget it. This cleaning method gets rid of the old varnish very well, but it will most likely get rid of a sizeable portion of most modern SU pumps as well, because the bodies are made from an aluminium based casting. The advice is a hang-over from the old days when the bodies of SU pumps were made from brass castings. In any case, caustic soda and strong nitric acid are not very nice things to have around.

If the deposit of varnish is light, scrubbing with methylated spirit or an aerosol of carb cleaner will shift it, and for getting inside the valve ports there are gum and varnish removing compounds available which do a good job safely, though please watch your eyes, and preferably wear goggles when you use them.

Start dismantling by taking off the plastic end cover, the one where the connecting wire goes. On the long terminal screw which holds it there are a number of washers, including a lead washer which squashes out when the nut is tightened, to make sure of a good

Below: At the base of the terminal screw is the lead washer which has to be cut off. You get a new one in the overhaul kit. Above: Start dismantling by taking off the unions, and watch for any in-line filters inside them.

electrical contact. This lead washer has to be cut away with a knife, and you must use a new one, which will be supplied in the overhaul kit, when you put things together again.

Take off the radio suppressor condenser if one is fitted, and the steel blade with one part of the contact points (it may be a single or a double set of points, depending on the model).

Now you can turn your attention to the other end and undo the ring of screws holding the two parts of the body together, but mark the parts before you do, so that you put them back in the same relative position. The number of screws may vary, and there may or may not be an earthing stud as well, depending on the model. There might also be an aluminium plate stamped with a number such as AUF200, which identifies the model of pump when you buy a repair kit. Don't lose it, it's all the identification you've got.

For the moment leave any filters or domed housings on the bottom part of the body. I'll deal with those in a moment. Take the two parts of the body apart carefully, over the bench as, if it's an old pump, there may be a number of brass rollers loose under the diaphragm. Collect and save them carefully, as they are not in the repair kit and not easy to obtain on their own. On later pumps you won't find brass rollers, you'll find a shaped nylon armature guide in place of the brass rollers. Hook the two ends of this nylon guide free from the recess under the diaphragm, and lift it out. Treat it carefully. Like the rollers, it's often difficult to obtain as a replacement part. Now you can unscrew the diaphragm and lift it out as an assembly together with its spring.

Going back now to the other end of the pump, take out the two screws which hold the black plastic rocker pedestal to the body, and lift it away complete with the rocker assembly. The assembly is held in place by a hardened steel pin which you just push out. Take it out and store it carefully, as the pump will never work properly, or at least not for long, with a soft wire substitute. Don't try to take the core out of the magnet in the tubular part of the body. There's no need to take it out, and it can only be replaced or centred with special tools.

Your repair kit will contain a new rocker set, new contact blade, various washers, including the lead washer, and should also contain an assembly diagram showing the order in which all the parts fit. If it doesn't, or you are not using a kit, make a careful note of the order in which all the parts came off.

When you come to put the new rocker assembly on to the plastic pedestal, push the steel pin in position and then check that the centre toggle spring of the rocker assembly is above the spindle which carries the white rollers. It's possible to get things upside-down so that the action binds instead of working freely. Sometimes you might find that the repair kit in its plastic bag has been handled a bit harshly in transit, and the rocker assembly has been pushed out of true, so that it binds on the plastic. If so, straighten it carefully with a small pair of pointed-nosed pliers. It's quite weak and bendy until it's held by the diaphragm rod, so take things gently.

The rest of the top assembly goes together in the reverse order of taking it apart, but there are a couple of things to keep in mind. The first is to remember to fit the lead washer, with the coned face of the nut towards the lead washer so that it's clamped like a pipe olive. The second is that when you put in the two screws holding

Some pumps have loose brass rollers under the diaphram. Be careful not to lose any.

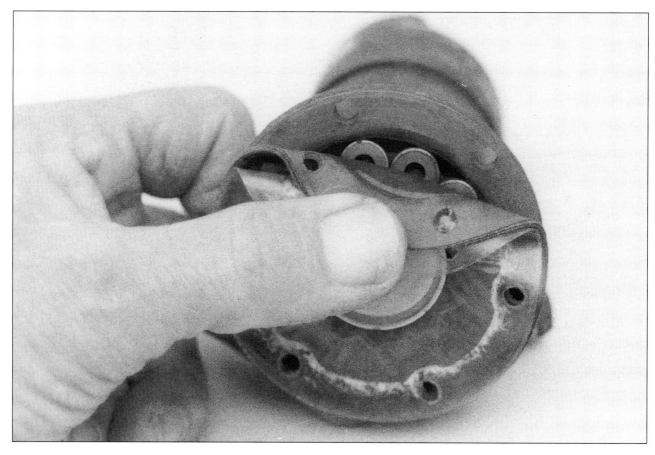

the plastic pedestal to the body, one holds an earthing tag. The spring washer goes between this tag and the pedestal, not on top of the tag. It makes a better electrical contact that way round. If there is a radio suppressor condenser, its tag takes the place of the spring washer. Don't overtighten the screws or you'll crack the plastic, and hold the earthing tag to stop it turning as there's a danger that it will be pulled, and twist off. Leave the contact blade off for the moment.

Go back to the other end of the body and fit the diaphragm, but before you do, fit the diaphragm spring in the housing with its smaller end towards the diaphragm, thread the small neoprene washer over the diaphragm spindle and seat it in the recess at the end. Now it's time to push the diaphragm spindle through the body and screw it into the trunnion in the rocker assembly. As it goes home you can check the action of the rocker by pushing the diaphragm spindle in and out against the spring. The rocker should toggle over cleanly and without binding on anything. Screw in the spindle until the rocker will no longer toggle over.

There are two types of rocker assembly, which I call an early and a late type. If you have the late type (see diagram) you have to fit the contact blade and check the rocker settings before you go any further. There are two stop fingers on these later rockers, one to stop its action against the pedestal and one to stop it against the body. Adjust the top stop finger so that when the points are in contact, there is a gap of between 0.030 in. and 0.040 in. (0.75 mm and 1.0 mm) between the top of the pedestal and the underside of the contact blade. Then adjust the bottom stop finger to give a gap between it and the top of the body of between 0.065 in. and 0.075 in. (1.65 mm and 1.90 mm). The fingers can be bent with a small pair of pliers to adjust them. When you have set the stop fingers, take the contact blade off again for the moment. The earlier type of rocker without the stop fingers doesn't have to be set, you adjust the points gap later if necessary.

Now, in either case you're ready to move on to the next stage. Put the brass rollers, if you have them, back under the diaphragm. If you have a nylon guide, you can leave it out for the moment.

Take care not to let any rollers fall out of position, hold the pump approximately horizontal, and push on the end of the diaphragm so that it can gently be unscrewed. Unscrew it a little at a time, as you carry on pressing, then releasing, the pressure until you get to the point where the rocker will just toggle over when you push. Now carry on unscrewing till the nearest holes line up, and then for a

Above: Most later pumps have a nylon ring instead of brass rollers. Below: Smaller pumps have gauze filters under a retaining plate at the bottom which also holds the pipe unions.

further four holes.

The diaphragm is now correctly set, and will not need any pre-stretching or flexing. Now push the diaphragm in and put a small fork wedge behind the rocker to hold the diaphragm in and prevent the brass rollers falling out while you attend to the other part of the body. If you have a nylon armature guide, set the diaphragm before you put it back in place.

With the main part of the pump reassembled, take the filters out of the bottom part of the body - they're under the unions on some types and under a screwed plug on others - and give them a good clean up in petrol. Take out the non-return valves, and if there's the slightest suspicion that they're not seating or working properly, renew them. Test their seating by alternately blowing and sucking at the unions. Make sure they, or the new ones, go back the same way that they came out, or your pump will try to work in the reverse direction, and not do it very well.

On all but the smallest type of SU pump there are valve

Above: On larger pumps there's often an empty chamber which helps to smooth the fuel flow.
Below: Again on larger pumps, be careful of these clear plastic diaphragms. They're easily damaged, but you shouldn't have to take them out.

devices under domed covers, the purpose of which is to smooth the fuel flow so that it doesn't come out in a series of spurts. If the inside of the body was clean, it's best to leave these flow-smoothing devices alone, but if you're using a gum and varnish remover, you'll have to dismantle these devices before you do. Take them apart carefully, and renew all the gaskets and neoprene washers. They don't normally come in a repair kit but you can get them from an SU agent.

He'll probably tell you that the pump should be flow and pressure tested after these flow smoothing devices have been disturbed. Strictly speaking he's right, but if you're careful with the reassembly there's every chance that the pressure and flow will be as they were before you disturbed them.

When you assemble the flow smoothing device which has a tapered spring inside, you should hold the spring compressed while you tighten the cover screws. The only way to do this is to make up a small wire tool as shown in the diagram. You push it through the hole in the domed cover, thread the spring over it, followed by the spring end cap and hook the end cap on the tool so you can pull the spring back while you put the cover on and tighten the screws. Be careful not to damage the internal washers and diaphragms when you turn the tool to take it out again.

With all the valves in the body reassembled you can marry the two parts of the body - lining up the marks you made before you took them apart - and put the screws in finger tight. Remove the wedge from behind the rocker before you tighten the body screws.

Refit the contact blade, and position it is just above centre when it meets the contact on the rocker. The blade is slotted to allow adjustment, as shown in the diagram.

On the early type rockers without stop fingers, the last job to be done is to set the points gap. Before you do this, set the blade so that with the points open it makes contact with the small ridge on the pedestal. Again, see diagram. Check the points setting indirectly by measuring the gap between the fibre rollers on the rocker and the body of the pump when the points are closed. It should be 0.030 in. (0.8 mm). If it isn't, bend the tip of the contact blade gently to adjust it, but make sure it still rests on the small ridge when the points are open.

The last job is to fit the end cover and the rubber band which seals it against moisture.

As an alternative to the SU, you can fit a Facet electric pump, an American make which is very popular with motor sport types and is imported into the UK by Fuel System Enterprises at Walton-on Thames in Surrey.

Facet makes two types of pump, a very compact little rectangular solid state one about three inches by two and half, and a larger one which they call an interrupter pump, a tubular one about two and a half inches diameter and five and a half inches tall.

It's called an interrupter because, like an SU electric pump, it has contact breaker points inside but, unlike the SU, you can't get at them to service them. They're in a sealed chamber inside the pump which is filled with argon gas so that the surfaces of the points don't oxidise. The only access to the pump is through the bottom cover which houses the filter and a magnet to trap any metal particles that might come over with the fuel.

The little solid state pump is very compact but it has one disadvantage, it has quite a low suction lift which means that it must be mounted not more than 12 inches above the bottom of the tank and, preferably, near the tank at the back of the car.

This isn't always convenient and, for this reason, I would recommend using the interrupter pump which has a higher lift, about 18 inches. It's still best to mount the pump at the back of the car because its 'push' capabilities are far greater than its 'suck' capabilities but it's usually quite happy working near the engine on the bulkhead provided it isn't mounted more than 18 inches above the bottom of the fuel tank.

There's one thing, though, that you must be careful about. Unlike the solid state pump which has two leads, negative and positive, coming from it, the interrupter pump has only one, the live or positive lead. Earth connection is made through the body of the pump. You either have to clean the paint off the back of the mounting bracket and the car's bulkhead to get a good contact or, better, clean the paint off one side of the front of the mounting bracket and run a separate earth wire from under a washer on the mounting bolt to a good chassis earth point.

There's been quite a lot of publicity recently about the possible dangers from fuel pumps which keep on pumping fuel through a fractured fuel line in the event of an accident after the engine has stopped but when the ignition is still on. This applies more forcibly to fuel injection system pumps which operate at a much higher pressure than electric pumps for carburettors but the danger could still be there.

These are the non-return valves in larger pumps. Make sure you get them back the right way round.

In their fixing instructions, Facet recommend that the electrical supply to the pump is routed via a pressure sensitive switch in the engine's oil gallery so that the pump will operate only when the engine has oil pressure. Normal cranking on the starter generates enough pressure to make the connection.

You can buy suitable switches to go in place of the oil pressure sender on your engine. They were, incidentally, fitted as standard on the Rover SD1, but I'm not sure if the threads will fit a Ford engine. A number of companies make them including the German instrument company VDO and, if you want to fit one, it's best to take your old oil pressure sender along to make sure that the threads are the same. There's no reason why you shouldn't fit one of these switches with an SU pump. Indeed there's every reason why you should.

You occasionally, but not very often, come across Facet pumps secondhand at autojumbles, but I've never seen one in a breaker's yard. In any case, you'd have to take a secondhand one on trust because you can't overhaul them. They're expensive, but they're good, and you get a good guarantee with them.

Chapter 12

ODDS AND SODS

Having covered the main areas in a typical kit car's
loom, here's a chance to look at a few accessories.

HAVING COVERED MOST OF THE GROUND ON KIT CAR
electrics, this chapter is by way of being a round-up of
odds and sods, mainly components that may have become
sluggish, or even decided not to work at all, from being
unused from the time the donor car was taken off the
road. Many small motors suffer from this malady and are
rejected because the local main dealer tells you they're
"unrepairable." What he means is that the bits inside
aren't listed in his microfiche because, at £20 plus an
hour, the labour cost of stripping the component down
and overhauling it would probably be higher than buying
a new one.

Sometimes, the component is genuinely beyond
economic repair but, provided you can take it apart,
there's no harm in opening it up and having a look inside.
Large numbers of components with motors inside them
are thrown away when a strip and clean would have given
them years of extra life. When you don't count your own

*Above Right: Two types of Ford central locking motor.
They're both master motors, but the one at the top is
the later one that bolts directly to the door latch. The
one below it, with the cable attached, operates the
lock through a wire rod and can be adapted to fit in
most doors. Below: Inside the two locking motor
casings. The motor itself is quite tiny, with most of the
space taken up by gearing and switch contacts.*

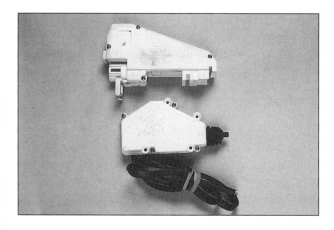

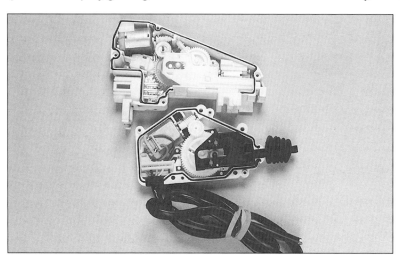

time it's worthwhile having a go. If, at the end of the day,
you have to throw it away or exchange it, you've lost
nothing but a few hours.

CENTRAL LOCKING

Central locking motors are a good case in point. Most
makes are similar, but I'll deal with the ones fitted to Fords
because they're popular, easy to fit to most doors – at
least, the earlier ones are – and there's a pretty good
supply to be found in breaker's yards so you can chop and
change and marry bits quite cheaply.

However, before you decide that the locking unit itself is
faulty, make sure that the door locking mechanism isn't so
stiff from lack of lubrication that the motor of
the locking unit isn't strong enough to
overcome the resistance. Another reason for
perfectly good locking motors failing to work,
and even sometimes playing silly buggers, is
that the door latching isn't lined up properly
so that, though the locking tries to work, it
can't complete its cycle. Locking motors
come in two types, masters and slaves.
Sometimes you have a master motor in the
driver's door only, and sometimes you have
two master motors, one in the driver's door
and one in the passenger's door so that
operating the key in either door operates the
central locking.

This is when you get attacks of the silly

buggers I mentioned earlier. You operate the key in one door, the other doors appear to lock and then unlock themselves again. In a few cases I've known them play like this for some time, locking and unlocking of their own accord till you open one of the doors. What often happens is that the second master motor tries to lock but, either because of a stiff mechanism or a misaligned latch it can't complete its lock cycle. After a second or so it senses that the door isn't locked so, being part of the central locking system it thinks that all the doors should be unlocked and sends a signal back to unlock all the others. However, the first master motor says to itself "I'm supposed to be locked", so it sends a signal back trying to lock the other doors again. The second master motor gets this signal, can't complete its locking cycle and back we go to square one.

In nearly all cases of this happening, the cure is to check the mechanism of both front doors to make sure that it isn't stiff and that the latch can work properly. Often, all that's needed in this case is to move the striker plate in slightly so that the door closes more firmly. It's always the master motors, or the doors in which the master motors are fitted, that cause this trouble. If a slave motor in the rear doors or the boot lid fails to work it's either the motor itself or sticking mechanism.

There is an exception to this, and that's on some Ford door locking motors fitted at the end of 1988 and beginning of 1989. Ford used two suppliers, one in Spain and one in France, and you can recognise the two types because on one the casing is held together with screws and can be taken apart whereas on the other, the casing is held by rivets and can't be taken apart. These two makes of motors didn't like each other very much and, if you happen to fit different makes of master motor in the two front doors they can sometimes start this lock-unlock business for no apparent reason. The answer here is change one of them for a matching motor.

You may also come across some old Ford locking motors with a black casing instead of the white casing of the later ones. These weren't fitted as original equipment as far as I know, but were a quite popular aftermarket fitting as Ford sold them in kits. If they're working OK, there's nothing wrong with using them again but, if they aren't working, they aren't very easy to find to cannibalise for parts. I wouldn't advise mixing and matching black and white motors in the car, particularly one black and one white master motor, even though they ought to be compatible.

An exploded drawing of a GM 'can' type wiper motor. In this case, the armature end float is controlled by the screw number 25. The sweep of the wiper blades is controlled by the length of the crank arm number 21.

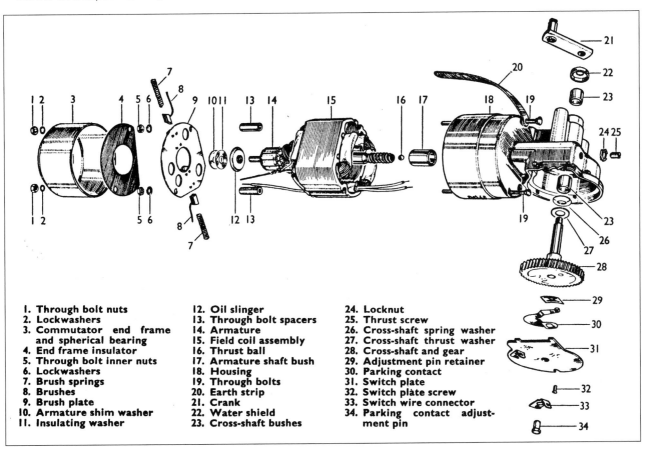

1. **Through bolt nuts**
2. **Lockwashers**
3. **Commutator end frame and spherical bearing**
4. **End frame insulator**
5. **Through bolt inner nuts**
6. **Lockwashers**
7. **Brush springs**
8. **Brushes**
9. **Brush plate**
10. **Armature shim washer**
11. **Insulating washer**
12. **Oil slinger**
13. **Through bolt spacers**
14. **Armature**
15. **Field coil assembly**
16. **Thrust ball**
17. **Armature shaft bush**
18. **Housing**
19. **Through bolts**
20. **Earth strip**
21. **Crank**
22. **Water shield**
23. **Cross-shaft bushes**
24. **Locknut**
25. **Thrust screw**
26. **Cross-shaft spring washer**
27. **Cross-shaft thrust washer**
28. **Cross-shaft and gear**
29. **Adjustment pin retainer**
30. **Parking contact**
31. **Switch plate**
32. **Switch plate screw**
33. **Switch wire connector**
34. **Parking contact adjustment pin**

To my mind it's better to stick with one type of motor throughout the car.

Oh yes, how do you recognise master and slave motors when they're off the car? Quite simple, the master motors have four cables coming from them and the slave motors have only two. One more point, if you get motors from a breakers you may well find that, on the more recent ones, the cable and its four-pin or two-pin plug are shorter than the earlier ones. It's just a quirk of Ford wiring that on later models the connecting cable reached further up into the door. Either you may have to extend the cable or, if it happens to be short, you can get an extension cable from most Ford dealers.

So far I've been talking about the older type of locking motor which operated the normal locking mechanism in the door via a wire rod link. Within the last few years Ford has changed over on most models to a different type of central locking motor which works the Ford PAT (Passive Anti-Theft) system. This motor is larger than the earlier type and doesn't operate the lock mechanism via a wire rod, it screws directly on to the latch itself. Also, it doesn't have any cables coming from it, there are connecting blocks into which the operating cable plugs. The master motors have six pins in this block, four for the locking and two for the engine immobiliser of the PAT system. Unless you're going to take over the whole door latch mechanism from the donor car, steer clear of this type of lock. They can't be adapted, or at least not adapted easily, to fit any latch mechanism other than the one they were designed for.

If you find that the motor itself doesn't work, even when you detach the wire rod from the lock, you've got two choices. Either you can get a few secondhand motors from a breakers and use one that works properly, or you can strip down a couple and see if you can build one good one from the two. The motor itself is quite small, most of the room inside the casing is taken up with gears and switching. If the motor itself works OK, the fault is probably in the plastic gearing which has become stiff with old grease or in the switch contacts which have oxidised.

WINDSCREEN WIPERS

A favourite cause of Lucas windscreen wipers not working, or working only very sluggishly, on a kit car when they worked perfectly well on the donor car, is that you've got the rack cable either running in too steep a curve or you've clamped it too tightly to the bulkhead so that the rack is binding in its outer tube. On other makes, such as Vauxhalls and some Fords, where the wipers are operated by a metal strap linkage, the fault is often that the linkage has become bent during the transfer from donor to kit car or that the pivot joints in the mechanism have become stiff. This is invariably the case if the motor seems to work OK for a time, then suddenly slows down and stops. Leave it for five minutes or so and it starts working again. In this case, the motor is fitted with a thermal cut-out switch, usually a simple bi-metallic switch and, though the motor is powerful enough to overcome stiffness in the operating mechanism, it runs too hot so eventually the thermal cut-out trips and the motor stops. Leave it to cool down, the thermal switch closes again and the motor works 'till it gets hot again.

On General Motors 'can' type motors fitted to most Vauxhalls, Opels and quite a few Japanese cars which use GM components, there's another reason why the motor sometimes runs hot and the thermal cut-out operates. These motors have self-aligning spherical bearings on the motor shaft and, if the motor's been dropped or banged while it was off the donor, the bearings may have been jolted out of line. The cure is very simple. Start the motor running and tap the sides of the can reasonably sharply a few times with a rubber or hide-faced mallet. Don't thump the life out of it, just a few smart taps are all that's needed to wake up the self-aligning bearings and tell them to get in line again.

If there's nothing wrong with the operating mechanism, and the bearings on GM motors are properly aligned, yet

Above: This Mini wiper motor has been modified for a GTM Coupe. It only drives one wiper arm and the gear wheel inside the motor has been changed in order to obtain the right 'sweep'.

the motor is still sluggish or works only in fits and starts, the most likely cause is a dirty commutator, often combined with sticking carbon brushes. The method of taking various makes of motor apart differs, some have plates you can take off while on others, like the round 'Ôcan' motors, you have to undo the bolts holding the casing and draw it off the end.

Once inside, you'll find a simple electric motor together with some sort of switching mechanism to control the fast, slow and intermittent wipe and operate the self parking when you switch off, quite often a thermal cut-out and several gears. Sometimes the gears operate the rack or link mechanism directly, and sometimes the operation goes through a crank arm. On most, though not all, motors you can alter the sweep of the wiper blades by changing either the crank arm or a pair of gears. This means that you can swap around between the same make of motor fitted to cars with different sized windscreens when you're looking to build up a good motor from several secondhand ones. In some cases you'll find that the part number is very similar with maybe the only difference being the last figure or letter, or perhaps a different figure or letter after a dash or a slash.

The dealer will tell you, of course, that you can't repair windscreen wiper motors, and he's most unlikely to have any spare parts in stock, though you may possibly be able to find carbon brushes for some Lucas motors at a Lucas agent. However, the brushes on wiper motors don't often wear down very much. After all, the motor's used only when it's raining, and most maladies can be cured by cleaning the commutator, making sure the carbon brushes are free in their holders and replacing old dried-up grease with new lubrication.

A dirty commutator can be cleaned in the same way as the commutator on a starter motor or alternator, with very fine glasspaper and, for the best operation, the mica segments between the copper parts of the commutator ought to be undercut slightly below the level of the copper. An old pen-knife blade ground down to form a very thin scraper is ideal for this job. The motor will still work if the mica insulation isn't cut back, but it won't last as long before needing another clean because carbon and copper dust can bridge the segments of the copper and short them out so that the motor looses power.

ELECTRIC WINDOWS

Many of the problems which afflict wiper motors also afflict electric window motors. They too suffer from sticking mechanisms, either the rack which operates the

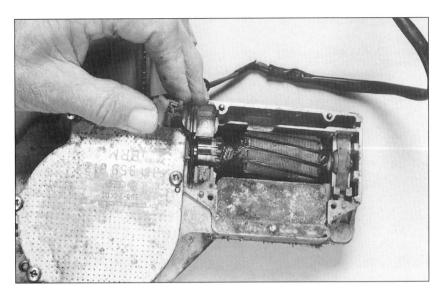

The inside of a window winding motor that has suffered from condensation. All it needed was a clean. The brushes lift out in their plastic holders, and the self-aligning bearing at the end of the Armature shaft is held by a large leaf spring.

lifting arm, or regulator as most makers term it, or from the glass of the window sticking in a well worn or distorted channel. So, once again, make sure all the operating mechanism is free and working properly before you blame the motor itself.

Window motors wear out even slower than wiper motors because they're called on to operate only for a few seconds at a time, and even then not very frequently. Some motors in rear windows may have worked only a

This is a large bulkhead-mounted heater blower motor with one large diameter central bearing, The armature lifts out when you separate the two halves of the casing, but watch out for shims and washers and make sure they go back in the same places.

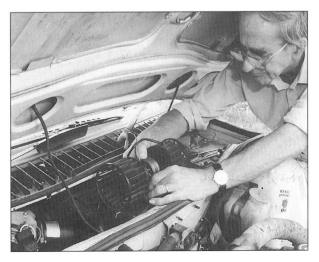

Don't be misled by the large size of the adjusting screw on some horns. It takes only a slight turn to alter the note from a clear tone to a strangled burp.

few times in their lives. When they go wrong it's almost certainly because of internal condensation which has oxidised the commutator or caused the carbon brushes to stick. Striping and cleaning Ñ or even just taking the cover plate off and cleaning Ñ is all that's needed to get them working again. In some cases where the motor box and the gearbox have separate covers there's no need even to disturb the gears.

You'll probably find that when you go to undo the screws of the motor cover plate your screwdriver will be drawn to the plate by the very strong magnet inside and, when you go to lift the plate off, you have to lever it up to get it clear of the magnet. Be careful, because many motors have cover plates that are held in position by two very tiny dowels, only a millimetre or so diameter, as well as the screws. Be careful not to bend these dowels when you lever the plate up. Watch out also for a gasket under the plate. It's there partly to keep out moisture but you'll find on some motors that it extends well inside the motor box and acts as an insulator to stop the edges of the carbon brushes from shorting out against he cover plate.

Like the GM Ôcan' wiper motors, many electric window motors also have spherical self-aligning bearings for the motor shaft, some times carried in a recess where they're held by a large leaf spring. Unlike the self-aligning bearings in GM motors, you shouldn't thump the bearings in an electric window motors to get them in line. Make sure the bearing is free to move in its seating, and then align it by turning the armature round and round till it runs freely.

HEATER MOTORS

Motors for heater blowers sometimes fit up on the bulkhead where they drive one or sometimes two blowers that look like squirrel cages, or they fit on the back of the

heater matrix and drive a fan. Because of their position, the casing is exposed to wet and sometimes salt-laden air, so corrosion of the motor shaft is quite common. If the motor's been left standing for a long time, maybe months after it came off the donor car, this corrosion can creep along the shaft into the bearings and make the shaft very stiff indeed. Then you often get a slow speed when the switch is telling you it should be fast, and possibly only a crawl round when the switch is on low or slow. The obvious answer is to take the motor apart and clean it. As with other small motors, clean the commutator and check the carbon brushes as well as making sure the shaft is free to turn in the bearings.

Some of the large motors mounted on the bulkhead have the casing in two halves, split horizontally and, when you take the screws out, the centre shaft and armature falls out together with the shims that control the end float. The motor will work, though it may be noisy with slightly too much end float, but it will stick and jam if there isn't enough end float. No doubt the makers have a figure for the end float, but you won't find it in any of the manuals because the motor isn't intended to be repairable. However, I've found that most small motors, in heaters as well as in wipers, window winders and other applications, work quite happily if the end float for the armature is about 0.005 to 0.010 inches. Measure it if you can, but usually you'll find that a just perceptible Ôshake' on the shaft from end to end with no lubrication is about right. When the bearings are running in grease, or the shaft is attached to some sort of gearing, it's difficult to feel the end float so use a feeler gauge to make sure there's freedom and the shaft isn't binding. If the end float goes tight and loose when you turn the armature either the shaft is bent, in which case the motor's useless, or the self-aligning bearings aren't in line.

HORNS

A horn which emits a strangled squawk rather than a steady clear tone is an embarrassment as well as being an MoT test failure. If cleaning the contacts at the terminals doesn't get it sounding healthy, there's usually an adjusting screw held by a large locknut. Sometimes this screw looks pretty massive, but don't be mislead. It takes only a small adjustment to alter the tone, so try it a quarter of a turn at a time and, when you get it right, make sure the screw doesn't move when you tighten the locknut.

Sometimes, even though the horn's working well, it sounds very harsh and sharp, almost with a ragged echo. If you find this, try mounting it with a flexible or semi-flexible pad between the horn and whatever it's screwed to. It doesn't need to be floating about, a pad of hard rubber or maybe just a strip of canvas belting between the horn and the chassis will improve the note no end by damping out the harsh overtones.

Chapter 13

WIRING - THE EASY WAY!

If dealing with wiring problems still sounds like a challenge you would rather avoid, then a purpose made loom might prove your salvation.

SO YOU'VE READ THIS BOOK AND THE THOUGHT OF making up or modifying an existing wiring loom still scares the living daylights out of you. Don't panic, all is not lost, as you can find solace in the fact that many kit car manufacturers these days offer made-to-measure looms for their kits. Forget trying to work out how a relay works or what fuse rating you need for a particular job, simply get out your cheque book and plug in a brand new purpose-built wiring harness.

These tailor-made looms can often be further customised for your own engine choice and dash switches etc. They usually come with full fitting instructions which should ensure it's a pain-free experience, except, of course, when you write out the cheque. Heading this route will typically set you back anything upwards of £150.

If that sounds a little too heavy then don't start panicking just yet. The chances are that the manufacturer's dedicated loom will have started life on the bench of wiring expert Trust Electrical. Trust now services the requirements of many of the industry's leading names but the company may also be able to offer you a slightly cheaper alternative to buying a dedicated loom for your own specific kit.

If you take a moment to look through any typical kit car magazine, you'll soon realise that the industry is actually split into three or four main types of car. There are the sevenesque kits, Cobra replicas, traditional tourers and mid-engined cars. A few others are scattered in between but by far the majority can be slotted into any of these four categories. Within any one of these areas the electrical layout of components is often extremely similar and minor tweaking for alternative engine installations will soon have the loom ready to slot into place. Because the looms aren't specifically designed for just one kit make, the kit car builder is expected to make up a few connectors etc, but then the price can come down slightly to a more reasonable £125+. Sound interesting? Then read on...

Trust Electrical was set up by Martin Griffin in around 1990 when he fell into the role by accident. A production and design expert in the circuit board industry, Martin was obviously undaunted by the subject that makes many of us quake in our boots and the attention to detail and high standards demanded by his previous occupation also have their obvious advantages when it comes to the rather more simple world of kit car electrics.

Martin has always been a car fan and even when he was building one-off specials in the 'seventies he was, not unsurprisingly, making up his own looms for them. When the inevitable kit car project approached in the late eighties he hadn't even contemplated doing anything else but making up his own wiring harness. When a friend of his, who just happened to be a kit car manufacturer, saw his work he asked Martin to make up some looms for a few of the kits he was building up at the time and, as they say, the rest is history. He now supplies looms for YKC, Gardner Douglas, Ginetta, Royale, Car Craft and a large number of other familiar

Martin Griffin, of Trust Electrical, assembling a wiring loom on a pin-board 'jig' to ensure it'll fit the intended car perfectly every time.

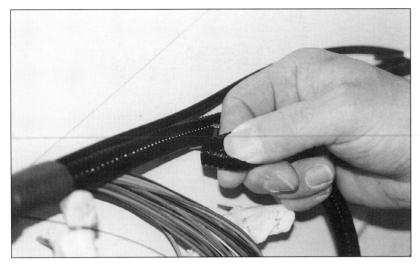

All Trust looms are bound in convoluted tubing. It's easier to work with and modify at a later stage whilst also being more flexible than conventionally wrapped looms thus making it more simple to fit.

builder. It's what he calls his Sierra Sport Wiring Loom which can be fine tuned for any Sierra based sevenesque kit. The loom comes complete with clear and concise fitting instructions and the first thing he recommends any customer to do is lay the loom out on the sitting room floor and familiarise himself with its layout. In the small box it looks a terrifying bird's nest of wires and connectors but spread out it soon begins to take some logical form.

The first thing I noticed was the distinct lack of traditional loom tape. Instead, Martin uses convoluted tubing to hold all the various wiring runs neatly together. The tubing is split down one side which makes putting

names. Plus, of course, he has the generic looms for sevens, Cobras etc. All in all, it makes him a very busy man.

At his base up in Harrogate, Martin pulls out a loom which is just about to be shipped out to a Robin Hood

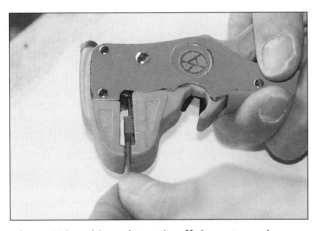

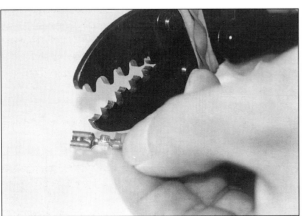

Above: Using this tool to strip off the outer casing on a cable will give far better results than any other method. Below: Use a proper crimping tool. The metal spade connector has two crimping points - one onto the wire and one onto the sleeve.

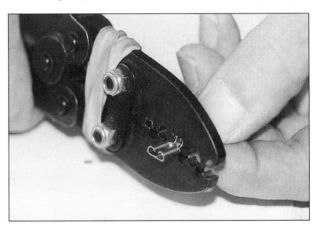

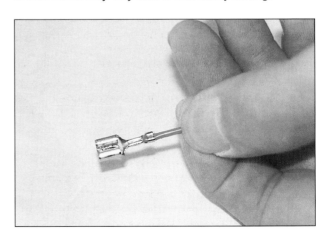

Above: Crimp onto the wire first and then onto the sleeve. It's the latter that gives the connector its resistance to coming apart. Below: The finished article looks very tidy and is extremely strong.

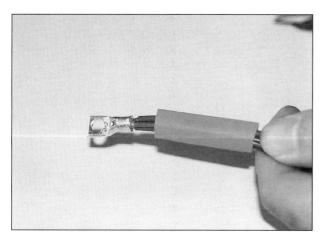

Trust uses PVC shrink wrap on the end of most wire runs. Above: Here you can see the length of shrink wrap chosen and what it will cover. Below: The PVC tubing is slid into place before being heat treated.

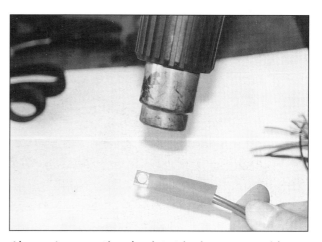

Above: A conventional paint stripping gun provides plenty of heat to cause the PVC to shrink. Below: The end result is highly professional. Adhesive shrink wrap can also provide a watertight seal.

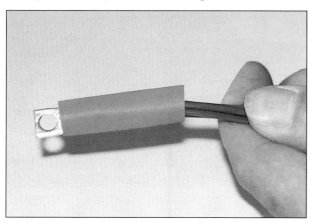

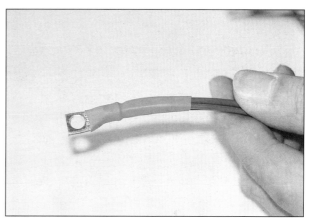

the wires in much easier and running individual wires out to their components much simpler. It also makes it easier for the car owner to make later modifications; none of this messy unravelling of miles of tape. Martin also finds that the tubing makes the loom less rigid than a tape wrapped harness, it's also easier to handle and fit whilst having a really neat and professional finish to it. All in all, it sounds sensible and looks terrific.

At all the ends where wires vacate the tubing you'll find either adhesive or non-adhesive PVC heat shrink tubing. The adhesive heat shrink is better at making a water tight seal, so you'll typically find this in and around the engine bay. At the end of any wires you find various spade, bullet and other types of connector but the surprise to anyone who has been told never to crimp but instead to solder all their connections is that Martin hand crimps everything.

As expected, he's vitriolic in his hatred of the cheap crimp tools you typically find in a Halfords boxed set. Rarely will they do the job properly and they certainly have a very short life span before the jaws start to bend out of shape. Rather more surprising is his equal hatred

for the ultra expensive ratchet type professional crimping tools you can buy for a cool £80. You can see from the photographs which ones he prefers and they can typically be bought for a rather more reasonable £30. What these do is give you the feel that apparently is lacking with the ratchet tool but the precision and robustness that is certainly non-existent with the cheapo ones.

But why crimp instead of solder? It's clear that you'll come across some people who swear crimping is the way to go while others will argue all night long that you can only be sure of a connection when it's soldered. For Martin, both methods are equally prone to corrosion problems but soldering can actually weaken the metal connector which may later cause it to snap in areas where it can come under stress, such as in engine bays etc. This is one of the reasons, apparently, that you won't find soldered connections in military aeroplanes. As for the strength of a crimped connection; I couldn't pull a crimped connector off a cable even when I was using a pair of pliers.

However, the success of the connection is all down to

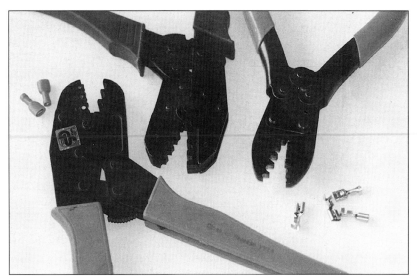

Above: Whilst you really must avoid using the cheap crimp tool found in boxed sets at places like Halfords, the expensive ratchet type crimpers aren't ideal. The one top right here is spot on. Below: Decent wire cutters are money well spent.

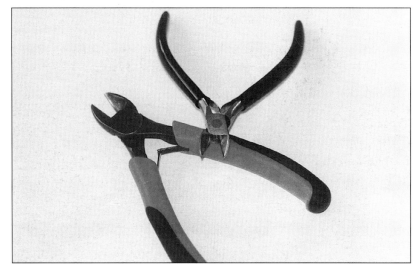

down evenly into the shroud.

Looking at the cable itself, all Trust looms are made of modern 'thin wall' cable. Gone is the old thick PVC shrouding and in its place a new PVC coating that makes the cables thinner, more abrasion resistant and the wiring itself capable of carrying heavier currents and operating at higher temperatures. Being thinner, it also makes the loom lighter as well as easier and less cumbersome to fit.

Most Trust looms come in three sections to make installation as easy as possible. The main part includes the front lights, engine and dash areas. There's then a long feeder cable that takes the necessary wiring back to the rear of the car. Even in the wide variety of seven-type kits, different cars are different lengths, so this section of the loom is left un-finished at one end so that it can be trimmed to the correct length to ensure a neat fitment. Don't panic about any complicated wiring though, as you'll simply be connecting all the wires into one multi-plug that comes with full instructions. The rear loom section plugs into this and completes the set-up.

It's the dash area of the loom that is certainly the most daunting to look at. There are connections for all the gauges, switches and warning lights you may want to use, along with the fuse box, relays and, possibly, column stalk connections. It's the latter that can cause greatest problems in a typical Sierra based loom. Ford was notorious for changing the way in which certain features worked, such as

using the crimping tool correctly. If you simply refuse to shell out on a decent crimping tool than Martin agrees that you'll be better off soldering your connectors. Equally, if you're not confident with a soldering iron, then it may be better to buy a decent crimping tool and go that route. So, what's the knack to getting a decent connection?

To start with, Martin uses a proper wire stripping tool and exposes only a tiny bit of the wire beyond its shroud. He uses the spade connectors that come in two sections; the metal part and a separate slide-on outer sleeve. These connectors have two connecting points that must be crimped, the first crimping down onto the wire while the second crimps down onto the PVC shroud. It's the latter that will give the connection its resistance to being pulled off and the 'ears' on the connector must bite

The finished loom can be held on with tie-wraps, sometimes along with these self-adhesive or screw-on mounts.

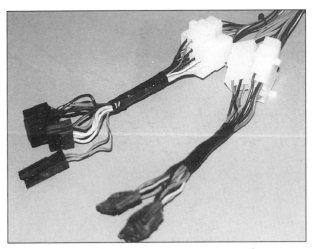

the indicators and hazard warning lights. To complicate matters further, it's impossible to source the plug-in connectors that Ford used for the column stalk controls. All of which means that Trust now asks that the kit builder supplies the column stalk plug-in connectors, along with several inches from the donor loom that went into the connectors, so that he can make-up the necessary loom modifications to ensure they work as expected. So, for all the potential headaches, Trust sorts them out so that you simply plug it all in.

And whilst I'm talking of retaining parts from the donor loom, it's also vitally important that you retain

Above left: Column stalk wiring can cause a few problems as the plugs cannot be bought separately. These are a customer's column stalk plugs which Trust wires into the finished loom (above).

things like the engine loom if you are using modern injected engines or turbo units. These are invariably separate plug-in sub-looms on the donor but they are

These multi-pin plugs are a real boon in the modern wiring harness and can make removal of components from the car so much easier.

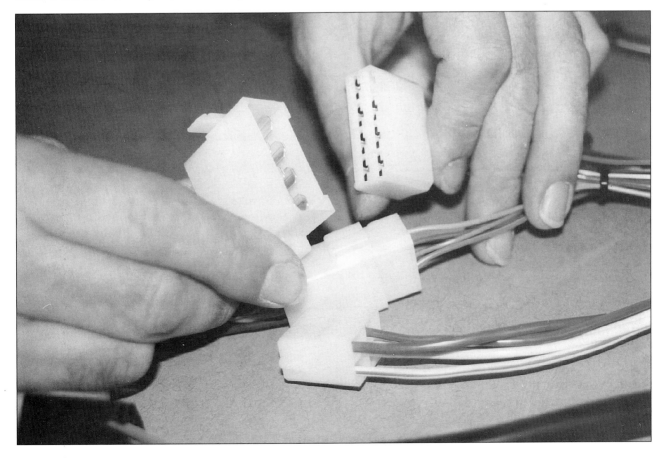

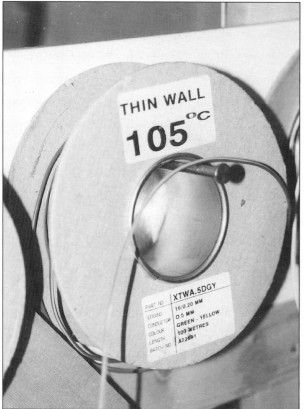

Above: One of the obvious advantages of buying a brand new loom is that fuse boxes etc are in tip-top condition. Left: All Trust looms are made with thin wall cable which has many advantages over the older wiring used in most donor car looms.

vital to any new loom as the connectors and also the control boxes that go with them cannot be bought separately. Martin has spoken to a number of people who have bought Cosworth engines from breakers without the sub-looms because the donor was fire damaged. However, breakers will never separate a good loom from another engine and Ford is likely to charge as much as the customer paid for the engine for a new wiring harness - you have been warned!

On every Trust loom are a number of features which the company feels should give the customer added confidence. To avoid any potentially disastrous meltdowns when the loom is being installed or in the event of connections coming loose or the car being involved in an accident, Trust always fits 50 amp strip fuses into the main battery feed cable. If a huge short does occur for any reason, this big fuse will blow and not only will the loom be saved from damage but potential fires and much worse hazards should also hopefully be averted. Other safety features include fusing the main and dipped beam circuit separately as well as fusing nearside and offside lighting circuits separately. If one of the fuses blows when you come to drive home late at night, at least some of your lights should work rather than losing the whole lot.

Many electrical problems on kit cars can often be traced to poor earths, so Trust has kept the number of earth connections in the loom down to a sensible minimum which is typically just three. At these points it is vital that the connection to the chassis is clean and tight, with no paint of chassis protection material between the contacts.

Trust also makes quite a play of the fact that all its looms are made to meet current Construction And Use Regulations. That means all looms include a dim/dip facility, indicator side light wiring and rear fog light wiring.

It is perhaps unsurprising that Trust is pretty sceptical about the benefits of retaining and modifying your old donor loom. Why use something that is perhaps fifteen years old which is designed for a completely different car with loads of features that you don't want in it and others that you do want not included? Cables, connectors and components do deteriorate with age and how do you know the condition of a cable that is hidden behind old and dirty loom tape? By the time you have fitted it into your new car, any number of cables may have twisted and snapped inside the tape leaving a veritable nightmare of testing and unravelling. There are no two ways about it, the arguments are certainly convincing...

But perhaps the most telling observation is this. Many kit car builders will spend thousands on shiny suspension components and chromed roll-over bars etc, and then

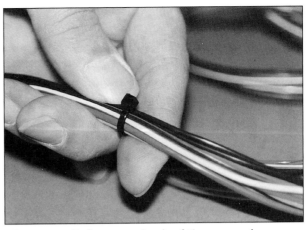

Above: You'll always use loads of tie-wraps when installing and modifying looms. Don't buy them in tiny packets of ten from Halfords. Find a shop where you can buy them by the hundred for a fraction of the cost.

use an ancient donor loom to save a few quid on the build cost. Poor wiring on a kit can be one of the worst problems you can come across, leading to endless unreliability. Why spend £15,000 on a beautifully presented Cobra replica only to have the car stranded in the garage because of the modified 1976 Jaguar XJ6 loom you fitted? You're right, it doesn't make any sense at all.

If you're tempted by one of Trust's generic looms the basic sevenesque looms costs £125, the Cobra type loom £150, the traditional roadster loom £145 and the mid-engined loom (POA) (all prices are + VAT and correct at the time of going to press). You'll find the company's address and telephone number at the back of this book under the Useful Suppliers directory.

ACCESSORY DIRECTORY

Featured here are all the accessory companies you may find of use in a typical kit car wiring project. There was no charge for each supplier's insertion so if anyone is missing, it's simply because we forget them or didn't know they existed!

WIRING

Autopoint – Unit 2a, 9 Cannon Lane, Tonbridge, Kent, TN9 1PP. Tel: 01732 357383

Custom Auto Looms Ltd – 29 Fowlmere Road, Foxton Village, Cambridge CB2 6RT. Tel: 01223 511023. Fax: 01223 514401.

Merv Plastics – 201 Station Road, Beeston, Nottingham NG9 2AB

MMT Electronics Ltd – Tel: 01453 731997

NF Auto Development – Redlands, Lindridge Lane, Staplehurst, Kent TN12 0JJ. Tel: 01580 891309. Fax: 01580 893733.

Premier Wiring Systems – Twin-Trees Business Park, Moor Lane, Westfield, Woking, Surrey GU22 9RB. Tel: 01483 715725

Trust Electrical – Tel: 01423 501393

Vehicle Wiring Products – 9 Buxton Court, Manners Industrial Estate, Ilkeston, Derby DE7 8EF. Tel: 0115 930 5454

INSTRUMENT SPECIALISTS

ETB Instruments – 17 Leighcliff Building, Maple Avenue, Leigh-on-Sea, Essex SS9 1DJ. Tel: 01702 711127

Saturn Industries – 10-14 Newland Street, Coleford, Forest of Dean, Gloucestershire GL16 8AN. Tel: 01594 834321

Speedograph Richfield – Rolleston Drive, Arnold, Nottingham NG5 7JR. Tel: 0115 926 4235. Fax: 0115 920 9912.

GENERAL PARTS SUPPLIERS

Anthony Stafford – Unit 53, Kepler, Off Mariner, Litchfield Road Trading Estate, Tamworth, Staffordshire B79 7SF. Tel: 01827 67714. Fax: 01827 60251.

Classic Spares Ltd – Unit 4 Brook Road, Britannia Road, Waltham Cross, Hertfordshire EN8 7NP. Tel: 01992 716236

Direct Specialist Supplies – Unit 3, 96-98 Dominion Road, Worthing, West Sussex BN14 8JP. Tel: 01903 232814

Europa Specialist Spares – Fauld Industrial Estate, Fauld, Near Tutbury, Burton on Trent, Staffordshire DE13 9HR. Tel: 01283 815609

Frost Auto Restoration Techniques – Crawford Street, Rochdale, Lancashire OL16 5NU. Tel: 01706 58619

Holden Vintage & Classic Ltd – Linton Trading Estate, Bromyard, Herefordshire HR7 4QT. Tel: 01885 488000

Merlin Motorsport – Castle Combe Circuit, Chippenham, Wiltshire SN14 7EX. Tel: 01249 782101

MISCELLANEOUS

Donor vehicle parts – Kit Fit. Tel: 01636 893453

Ignition systems - Autocar (Electrical Equipment Co. Ltd), 49/51 Tiverton Street, London SE1 6NZ. Tel: 0171 403 4334. Fax: 0171 378 1270.

Instrument refurbishment and cable modification – Speedy Cables, The Mews, St. Paul Street, Islington, London N1 7BU. Tel: 0171 226 9228

General garage tools – Machine Mart. Tel: 0115 956 5555 for a catalogue and to find your nearest dealer.

Which KIT?

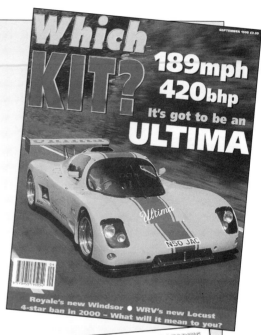

UNQUESTIONABLY BRITAIN'S LEADING KIT CAR MAGAZINE

Up to 100 pages every month

- Full road tests
- Detailed kit build-ups
- In-depth technical features
- Readers' cars
- Latest models
- All the latest news
- Fascinating historical features
- Club news
- Loads of classified ads
- Competitions

Index

About the authors

Peter Wallage (pictured) has spent all of his working life in and around cars and the motor industry. He worked in the design offices of Rolls Royce and Scammell, then for a design consultants before turning full time to motoring journalism in 1964. Along with his son, John, who provides the technical photographs, Peter now writes in a number of well known monthly motoring magazines including *Fast Ford*, *Ford Heritage*, *Mini Magazine*, *Practical Motorist* and *Which Kit?*

Major kit car shows you may like to visit include:

THE SPORTS & KIT CAR SHOW - A large indoor event held at Stafford County Showground every year in mid-March and featuring displays by over 40 kit manufacturers, 70 or more accessory and parts traders and loads of kit car clubs.

THE NATIONAL KIT & PERFORMANCE CAR SHOW - Held at Donington Park in mid-September every year, this is the kit car industry's major showcase event. Expect displays by up to 60 kit car manufacturers, over 50 parts and accessory traders and over 50 kit car clubs. A major attraction is the racing circuit which is used by company demonstrators and privately owned kit cars over the whole weekend. A superb event!

For further information on both these events contact the organisers:
**Limelight Exhibitions Ltd.,
1 Howard Road, Reigate, Surrey RH2 7JE.
Tel: 01737 225857   Fax: 01737 240185.**